The Original Face

The Original Face

AN ANTHOLOGY OF RINZAI ZEN

TRANSLATED AND EDITED BY

Thomas Cleary

GROVE PRESS, INC./New York

First Edition 1978
First Printing 1978
ISBN: 0-394-17038-5
Grove Press ISBN: 0-8021-4160-9
Library of Congress Catalog Card Number: 77-91354

Library of Congress Cataloging in Publication Data
Main entry under title:

The Original face.

1. Rinzai (Sect)—Addresses, essays, lectures.
I. Cleary, Thomas.
BQ9366.074 294.3'927 77-91354
ISBN 0-394-17038-5

Manufactured in the United States of America

Distributed by Random House, Inc., New York

GROVE PRESS, INC., 196 West Houston Street, New York, N.Y. 10014

CONTENTS

INTRODUCTION

A fundamental experience and comprehension which the enlightened Zen masters have urged us to realize is known as the original face. A famous Zen patriarch asked, "Before your father and mother were born, what was your original face?" If we understand "father and mother" in a traditional symbolic way to refer to ignorance and craving, this question directs us to realize our original nature as it was before a lifetime of habitual illusions based on ignorance and greed.

Here, in this original face, there is no station or grade, no prejudice, no philosophy or religion; all beings are the family, all worlds are the household. Only on the basis of the most fundamental realization, only with an open mind and heart, can the affairs of the family and household have a sound foundation for accomplishment.

This volume, titled *The Original Face* to evoke this persistent theme, draws on the sayings and writings of Zen masters who gave up their personal selves to find the truth and have been pointing at this original face for centuries. While awakening to the source of the one true reality is considered the main essential, as the trends of individual minds differ, so do methods of guidance; both universal and specific pivotal points are usually always included in Zen teachings, so that it is possible to pass from what one needs to awaken on his own to what one needs to be helpful to others.

The first section of this volume presents works of some of the pilgrims and founding fathers of Rinzai Zen in Japan: Rankei Doryu, National Teachers Daio and Shoitsu, and Jakushitsu Genko.

Zen Master Daikaku, Great Enlightenment, Rankei Doryu (Lanxi Daolong, 1213–1279) was born and began his studies in western China. After learning the Buddhist scriptures in various places, he studied with several Chan masters, finally realizing enlightenment with master Wuming Huixing. Having heard that Zen was not well known in Japan despite the flourishing of other teaching traditions of Buddhism, master Lanxi crossed the sea with several disciples. At this time he was thirty-three years old, and he spent another thirty-three years teaching in Japan. He died at sixty-six, leaving some twenty-four enlightened successors. His treatise on meditation strongly emphasizes what may be called the "round and sudden" aspect of *zazen* as realization.

National Teacher Shoitsu (1202–1280) began to study Tendai Buddhism when he was eight years old. Later he studied Zen and esoteric (Shingon) Buddhism in Japan before traveling to China when he was thirty-four to study Chan. Shoitsu was enlightened under the guidance of the renowned Chan master Wujun and subsequently spent time refining his practical understanding in the company of several other Chan masters in various places in China. Returning to Japan at the age of forty, Shoitsu served as abbot to a number of Zen and doctrinal school monasteries and produced more than thirty enlightened disciples.

National Teacher Daio (1235–1309) became a monk at age fifteen and went to study with master Rankei in Kamakura; at twenty-five he traveled to China and called on several eminent Chan masters. While serving as guest prefect in the assembly of master Xutang Zhiyu, one night as he rose from meditation he was suddenly enlightened. He wrote:

When suddenly mind and environment are both forgotten
There is the ability to penetrate freely earth,
mountains and rivers.
The whole substance of the real body of the king
of Dharma is manifest—
People these days face it without knowing it.

After returning to Japan, Daio again stayed with Rankei; later he taught in several large monasteries. Among his numerous successors was the famous National Teacher Daito, who concealed himself for twenty years before appearing in the world, according to Daio's instructions. The teaching line of Daio, Daito, and Daito's heir Kanzan is known as the O To Kan school of

Zen and is the source of present day Rinzai Zen in Japan.

Jakushitsu (1290–1367) was the last noted Japanese Zen master to go to China. Exceptionally intelligent, he became ordained at the age of fifteen and before long came to the National Teacher Butto, a Zen master in Kamakura. Butto said that the night before Jakushitsu's arrival he dreamed the saints appeared, their lights brightly illumining mountains and rivers; seeing Jakushitsu, Butto named him Genko, Original Light. Once when Butto was ill, Jakushitsu, who took care of his medicine, asked him what is the last word; Butto slapped him, whereupon Jakushitsu attained enlightenment. He was then eighteen years old.

Later Jakushitsu went to Yuan China and met Mingben, the foremost Linji Chan master of the time there. Subsequently he met numerous Chan masters and was praised and encouraged by them all. After he returned to Japan, he left a rich record of verbal and written teaching. He was especially noted for his eloquence.

By the closing decades of the fourteenth century, with the ending of the era of pilgrims and patriarchs in Japan, Zen was losing its freshness—indeed, it had already been in decline and become outwardly highly formalized in China by the time it took root in Japan. Social and politico-economic conditions were not very peaceful in either China or Japan, and much of the real Zen practice and teaching was carried on in places other than the large urban public monasteries. *Koan* study and practice seems to have become highly formalized, producing a great deal of Zen culture—literature, art, ritual—as an accumulating by-product. The Zen monks preserved formal knowledge, including worldly knowledge, while generations of warlords fought throughout the country. In the meantime, a few great masters furthered contacts with the populace, more and more writing in the vernacular.

Bassui (1326–1387) studied for a long time and experienced transformations of his state dozens of times before his great enlightenment. Later he furthered his investigation with the leading Soto Zen master of the day and did not assume the role of a teacher until his latter years. A volume of sermons and letters of advice to both homeless and lay students, written in easily understood, ordinary language, have been useful to many generations of meditators. Bassui favored an intense introspective method, continually transcending conscious ideas of understanding or realization, describing a method for gaining access to enlightenment and deepening one's practice to thoroughly awaken the original mind in all activities.

Ikkyu (1384–1481) is perhaps the best known and beloved of all Zen monks in Japan. He is the Nasrudin of Japan, and indeed some of the same tales and jokes are told of the humorous Sufi and the wild high priest of Zen. The bastard son of an emperor, Ikkyu was ordained at the age of six and realized enlightenment only after many hardships and difficulties. While the hundred years' war raged around the ancient capital of Kyoto, Zen was in decline and the monasteries corrupt; Ikkyu burned the testimonial of enlightenment he received as the sole successor of his teacher and suggested that he was the only true heir of Rinzai in sight at the time.

Ikkyu is famous for enjoying women and wine, especially in his latter years, flouting the pretexts of immoral abbots of his time. Carrying a wooden sword in public, he declared that the teachers of the time did not even have the sword to kill (egoism) much less the sword to give life (to enlightenment). For the last ten years of his life he was abbot of a major Zen monastery in Kyoto, but he never recognized any successors.

Ikkyu was a poet, calligrapher, and artist. His *Skeletons,* in prose and poetry, is a simple yet profound and utterly moving work.

Bunan (1603–1676) studied for thirty-odd years with the guidance of the famed National Teacher Gudo, considered the true lamp of the generation spanning war and peace. Bunan was a layman until his forties, working as a gatekeeper; there he used to talk to Gudo, who stopped there on his travels between east and west Japan, answering the request to teach. Later Bunan left home and became a monk and an abbot of a small hermitage, historically the foremost of Gudo's twenty-four successors.

Bunan had a few close disciples and a wide range of

disciples and acquaintances; he left a great deal of inspiration and guidance in Japanese poetry and booklets in prose and verse. He was naturally austere, led his group with a few simple rules; it is said that he couldn't even read the difficult Chinese classic texts. His greatest disciple was Dokyo Etan, later known as Shoju Rojin, or Old Man of Correct Perception, who was Hakuin's root teacher. Shoju Rojin seems to have been modest and austere like his teacher, whom he met when he was nineteen, three years after his first enlightenment, and went into seclusion in the Japanese Alps rather than accept abbacy in a monastery. He was evidently very learned and delved profoundly into the ancient teachings in his meditations; his disciple Hakuin shared this trait along with the everyday conversational manner of Bunan.

Bankei (1622–1693) wandered for years, sat for years, and visited teachers all over Japan before becoming suddenly enlightened at the age of twenty-six. He had been induced out of a hut in which he had been shut for two years, near death from consumption, and suddenly awakened while washing his face. Later he studied with a Chinese Chan teacher in Nagasaki, and at thirty years of age experienced great enlightenment there; of all the students there, he alone received the recognition of the Chinese master, and like others in similar situations, took his teacher's advice to slip away in the night. After this, Bankei remained in concealment for many years, after finding, as had Shakyamuni, that no one could understand his freshly inspired proclamations of what he had realized.

Later Bankei became an immensely popular teacher, the most famous of the time, said to have had over ten thousand disciples from all walks of life and all religions. Many established teachers of Zen, Vinaya, Shingon, Tendai, and Pure Land schools came to see and study under Bankei, who did not use ancient texts, but based his teaching on the fundamental unborn enlightened mind inherent in everyone, the aware radiance that is the source of both delusion and enlightenment. Sometimes called a popularizer because of his extensive teaching in the provinces and contact with all sorts of people, Bankei approved of very few successors. He said that there were enlightened peasants surpassing the teachers in the monasteries. Bankei's visible succession waned and died out in time, but his broad appeal, impeccable dignity, and fresh approach cut through much doctrinal and stylistic formality inherited from medieval Zen establishments, thus clearing the way for the monumental work of Hakuin and his successors.

Hakuin (1686–1769), called the greatest saint to appear in the last five hundred years in Japan, was the father of modern Rinzai Zen. Like Bankei, Hakuin and his enlightened apprentice and successor Torei (1721–1792) both went through exhausting years of effort; Hakuin's first awakening took place when he was twenty-four, his great awakening at twenty-seven, and his final realization at forty-three. Torei, like Ananda of old, was first awakened as he began to lie down, exhausted and driven to distraction by his intense efforts in sitting meditation; later he met Hakuin, but became desperately ill and had to be healed before continuing his work with Hakuin.

Hakuin, Torei, and other associates and successors revitalized the use of *koan* in Zen practice, making use of their extensive knowledge of the ancient teachings and experience in methods used all over Japan. Torei also wrote a detailed history of Zen and a study of the five houses of classical Zen in China, while Hakuin's works like the one presented here lucidly and powerfully show the reality of the teachings. Both Torei's and Hakuin's treatises are organized on the patterns of ancient teaching devices; they deal with fundamental and essential ideas, experiences, and scope of the Mahayana, or great vehicle teaching of enlightenment.

There is a great deal of anecdotal lore, written and orally transmitted, surrounding the hosts of Zen eminents which has been, is, and will be told in various books and circles. For the moment of this glimpse of the Original Face we emphasize not personalities or situations, but the timeless teaching. When the timeless teaching becomes familiar, it contains the personalities and situations in prototype, in the intimate or differentiating teachings of Zen after enlightenment.

This book contains materials suitable for deepening the study of such Zen classics as the *Blue Cliff Record,*

Mumonkan, and the letters of Ta Hui, translated in *Swampland Flowers* * and they, in turn, hark back to this book. It is safe to say that all the Zen masters represented in *The Original Face* were familiar with these books; Hakuin and Torei made famous commentaries on the *Blue Cliff Record,* sometimes called the foremost classic of Zen, and were certainly inspired in their practice and teaching by the stories and methods told in the Mumonkan (Gateless Gate or Barrier of the Gate of Nothingness) and the letters of Ta Hui, one of the great disciples of Yuanwu (author of the *Blue Cliff Record),* known as the second coming of Linji (Rinzai). All of these, therefore, are recommended to the reader.

* *Swampland Flowers: The Letters and Lectures of Zen Master Ta Hui,* translated by Christopher Cleary, published by Grove Press.

Zen Master Daikaku's Treatise on Sitting Meditation

Sitting meditation is the method of great liberation; all the teachings flow forth from this, myriad practices are mastered this way. Supernormal powers, knowledge, wisdom and virtue all arise from here, the path of life of humans and gods opens herein; all the buddhas have entered and left by this door, bodhisattvas practicing it have entered this door, disciples and self-enlightened ones are still only halfway there, while outsiders, though they practice, do not enter the right path. Whatever esoteric or exoteric schools do not practice this do not have anyone who realizes the way of buddhahood.

"What does it mean that sitting meditation is the root source of all the teachings?"

Meditation is the inner mind of the enlightened ones, discipline is their outer character, doctrine is their speech, Buddha remembrance is the invocation of Buddha's name—all come from the enlightened mind of the buddhas; therefore it is considered fundamental.

"The method of meditation is formless and thoughtless; spiritual qualities are not obvious, and there is no proof of seeing reality—so how can we believe in this?"

Your own mind and the enlightened mind are one—is that not spiritual quality? If you don't know your own mind, on whom can you call for witness and proof? Other than the identity of mind and Buddha, what proof do you seek?

"How can the ability to cultivate the teaching of one

mind compare to myriad practices cultivating myriad virtues?"

When you suddenly awaken to the pure clear meditation of those who realize thusness, the six transcendences and myriad practices are complete within your body; thus the one practice of meditation includes all practices. Haven't you heard it said that the three realms are only one mind, that outside of mind there is nothing else? Even if you do cultivate myriad practices, if you don't know the mind you cannot realize enlightenment; and how can there be any way to fulfill the way of the Buddha if you don't realize enlightenment?

"How should we practice this method? Even if we practice we are not sure of attaining enlightenment and fulfilling buddhahood; and if it is uncertain, even if we do practice, what is the benefit?"

This school is an exceedingly deep and subtle teaching; once you have heard it, it becomes an excellent cause for enlightenment for all time. An ancient said, "Those who hear this, even if they don't believe, have blessings greater than humans or gods; those who study even without attainment eventually reach buddhahood." This teaching is the school of the enlightened mind; the enlightened mind itself basically has no delusion or enlightenment. This is actually the subtle art of those who realize thusness; even if you don't become enlightened, when you sit once in meditation you are a buddha for that sitting; when you sit for a day in meditation you are a buddha for a day; when you sit in meditation all your life, you are a buddha all your life. The same is true of the future; one who can have faith in this is someone with great potential.

"If so, I can practice, too; how should I rest my mind, how should I use my mind?"

The enlightened mind has no attachment to appearances; detachment from appearances is the character of reality. Among the four modes of conduct—walking, standing, sitting, and lying—sitting is considered to be stable and tranquil. This means sitting straight and contemplating the characteristics of reality.

"Please explain in detail the meaning of sitting straight and contemplating reality."

Sitting straight means sitting cross-legged as the Buddhas do; contemplating reality means sitting meditation—forming the symbol of absorption in the cosmos,* body and mind unmoving, eyes half-open, watching over the tip of the nose, you should see all compounded things as like dreams, illusions, bubbles, shadows; don't get hung up in thought about them.

"Crossing the legs and making the symbol with the hands is the comportment of the realized ones, but why keep the eyes half-open, watching over the tip of the nose?"

When the eyes are open and you can see for a distance, your mind can be distracted by the profusion

* Left palm up, left hand on right palm, thumbtips joined to form a circle, symbol of the body of reality with no lack or excess, beginningless and endless, perfect and complete as a sphere.

of objects; yet if you close your eyes, you fall into a state of darkness and oblivion, and your mind is not clear. When your eyes are half-open, your thoughts don't race; mind and body are one thusness. When you examine clearly, the afflictions of birth and death cannot be approached—this is called fulfilling buddhahood right where you are, the meaning of great capacity and great function.

"Though I hear what you say, it's still hard to really believe. Only by accumulating the virtues of reading and reciting scriptures and spells, fasting, discipline, and recitation of Buddha names, can we have something to rely on; how can there be anything special about peaceful meditation without doing anything?"

Such doubt is called activity causing birth and death; such doubt is called affliction. Practicing everything without any sense of attainment is called the exceedingly profound transcendent wisdom; this wisdom can cut off the source of birth and death, like a sharp sword. To practice virtue in hopes of reward is the illusion of ordinary folk; bodhisattvas do not seek for the resulting rewards as they cultivate roots of virtue, because they cultivate goodness for the sake of impartial love and compassion, and thus it becomes sustenance for enlightenment. As for those who seek rewards as they cultivate virtue and attain the lesser reward of humanity or godhood, this is surely the work of birth and death.

"Without accumulating virtue and good qualities, how can one become a Buddha, in whom myriad virtues are complete?"

It takes three incalculable eons to attain buddhahood by accumulating virtue and good qualities, but if you practice the way of unity of cause and effect, you realize buddhahood in one lifetime. Someone who illumines his own mind and awakens to his real nature sees that he himself is originally Buddha, not now attaining buddhahood for the first time.

"Do those who realize buddhahood by seeing reality not depend on cause and effect? Should they not cultivate virtue?"

Although those who realize buddhahood by seeing their true nature may cultivate virtue, they do it for others' benefit, not for rewards. Because they teach and transform sentient beings, they teach cause and effect; because they know they have no personal gain, they do not depend on merit—they have no mind at all.

"What is no mind? If there is no mind at all, who sees reality, who awakens to the way? And who can expound the way to teach?"

No mind means that there is no deluded, foolish mind; it does not mean there is no mind to discern false from true. If one doesn't think of sentient beings, doesn't long for Buddhas either, doesn't think of illusion or seek enlightenment, doesn't go along with the honor of others, does not hope for fame, profit, support or reputation, does not shrink from attacks from those who are resentful or hostile, and does not add any discriminating thoughts about any good or evil, one is called a mindless wayfarer. Thus is it said, "The path is mindless of union with man, a mindless man unites with the way."

"Are there differences of more or less merit in fasting, observing the precepts, reading and reciting scriptures and spells, and chanting Buddha names?"

Eating once a day removes greed for food and results in great blessings and virtue in the coming life. Morality and discipline is also to stop bad states of mind and produce a good mental state; those with good minds live in human and heavenly realms, in the highest estates. Since those who read the scriptures and spells protect and maintain the teachings of the enlightened ones, these people will have great knowledge and wisdom in the coming life. Extolling their names is taking refuge in the Buddhas, so in the coming life one will surely be born in a Buddha land. No mind is the Buddha mind; the qualities of this enlightened mind cannot be reached by words or thought—it is truly inconceivable.

"Such roots of goodness as these each have their merit, undoubtedly, but what is the virtue of mindlessness?"

Learning the standards of conduct of the Buddha, transmitting the sayings of the Buddha, and extolling the names of the Buddha have merit, so mindless wayfarers must also have merit; if you say no mind has no merit, then other practices cannot have any merit either. All roots of virtue and good qualities are conditional, whether they be heavenly or humanly mundane; no mind is immediate witness of the path of enlightenment, so its merit cannot be adequately expressed in words—really it is the condition of the one great matter; the afflictions of birth and death die away of themselves, mind and body are one thusness—this is what it is. How can there be any doubt about the immediate mind realizing buddhahood? That is why someone in ancient times said, "To make offerings to the Buddhas of the three times cannot compare to making offerings to one mindless wayfarer." Actually this is the sphere which only an enlightened one can communicate to an enlightened one; ordinary people, disciples, and self-enlightened ones cannot fathom it.

"The scriptures do not speak of no mind, nor do they praise it; by what school of teaching do you esteem this?"

Various scriptures have not failed to speak of it; some say "the path of words ends," some say "it cannot be explained," or "ultimate emptiness," or "the condition of the one great matter." And also they say that all things are quiescent and dead—Shakymuni shut his room, Vimalakirti closed his mouth. Does this not point to no mind? Because the phantomlike bodhisattvas already have experiential knowledge of this, the Buddha does not preach it to them, and he does not teach it to seekers of sainthood and self-enlightenment because they could hardly attain it. That is why it says in the Lotus of Reality scripture, "Do not expound this scripture in the presence of ignorant people." That's what this means. Although there are eighty-four thousand entrances to the truth in the teachings, they do not go beyond matter and emptiness. Everything that has form and characteristics is matter, body; that which does not show any form is all empty. Because the body has form, it is called material; and because the mind is formless, it is called empty. All the scriptures do not go beyond these two things: matter and emptiness. They can't explain the sphere of no mind, so they don't extol this matter. Because words cannot reach it, it is called the special transmission outside of doctrine.

"Is this body then to be considered illusion? Can it be considered enlightenment? And what is the mind? The basis of illusion and enlightenment, it should be known. And is the mind inside the body or outside the body? Where does it come from?"

The body of four gross elements (fire, water, earth, air) and five clusters (matter, sensation, perception, coordination, consciousness) fills the universe; all sentient beings are the foundation. Causes and conditions interact to form physical bodies—this is called birth. When the results of the causes and conditions change and die out, then the four elements disperse—this is called death. In form and characteristics there are ordinary people and saints; in the essence of mind there is no delusion or enlightenment. Even so, we provisionally define the deluded as sentient beings and the enlightened as the buddhas. Delusion and enlightenment just depend on the deceiving mind—in the real mind there is no illusion or enlightenment. Sentient beings and buddhas are basically deluded or enlightened on the basis of one mind; when you comprehend its true nature, then ultimately there is no distinction between ordinary man and saint. Therefore the Surangama scripture says, "The perfect illumination of inconceivable reality is beyond names and symbols; there are no original world or sentient beings."

"If there is fundamentally no illusion in the nature of mind, where do illusions come from?"

When false thoughts arise, illusion comes along, and because of illusion, afflictions are born. When errant thoughts cease, then illusion goes; and when illusion goes away, afflictions also die out. Afflictions are things of life, seeds of birth and death. Enlightenment is the way to extinction. If you take peace and quiet to be bliss, all things are afflictions; but when you are enlightened, all things are enlightenment. People of the world do not understand this basis of delusion and enlightenment; they suppress thoughts of birth and death and think that this is the nonbirth of a single thought, and also consider this mindlessness—but these are still thoughts of birth and death, not mindlessness, not quiescence. When you try to stop thought by thought, birth and death continue.

"Those of the lesser vehicle fall into the principle of emptiness and so don't know mindlessness; can bodhisattvas of the great vehicle attain this no mind?"

Through the (highest) tenth stage, bodhisattvas still have two kinds of obstruction—confusion and knowledge; therefore they do not realize no mind. The obstruction of confusion means that bodhisattvas up to the seventh stage still have conscious seeking for truth, and that becomes a barrier. Up to the tenth stage, they have conscious shining awareness, which thus becomes a barrier. When they reach the stage of complete enlightenment, they merge with this no mind.

"Since even bodhisattvas through the tenth stage do not know this, how can beginning students merge with no mind?"

The great vehicle is inconceivable, directly cutting off the root source of a thought; there are those who awaken to it immediately. In the doctrinal schools they set up three stages of sagehood and ten stages of sainthood for those of dull faculties and potential; there are people of sharp faculties who immediately become truly awake when they are first inspired and directly attain buddhahood. Merging with no mind when reaching the tenth stage of bodhisattvahood and true enlightenment is no different in principle from the no mind we speak of now in seeing the true nature and realizing buddhahood.

"In seeing real nature and realizing buddhahood, what is the way, what is real nature, and how does the seer see? Can it be known by knowledge? Can it be seen by the eye?"

Knowledge attained by studying scriptures and treatises is discriminating knowledge from seeing, hearing, discerning, knowing; this practice does not need such knowledge. Turning the light around to shine back, knowing and seeing fundamentally inherent nature, is called the eye of wisdom; after seeing nature, seeing, hearing, discernment and knowledge may then be put to use.

"In knowing and seeing one's own fundamental inherent nature, the knowing and seeing can be known, but what about inherent nature itself?"

Because all sentient beings have a fundamental nature, it supports their own bodies; this real nature has never been born, never dies, has no form or shape, is permanent and unchanging—this is called fundamental inherent nature. Since this inherent nature is the same as that of all buddhas, it is called Buddha nature. The three treasures (buddhas, their teachings, their communities) and six kinds of sentient beings (humans, gods, ghosts, animals, titans, hell beings) all have this nature as their basis, whence come to be myriad things.

"What is turning the light around to shine back?"

Illumining outward things, one's own light is turned back to shine on the inner self. The mind is bright as the light of sun and moon, immeasurable and boundless, shining on all inner and outer lands; where the light does not reach is dark—this is called the ghost den on the black mountain, the abode of all ghosts, which can hurt people. The mind phenomenon is also like this; the light of knowledge of the mind essence is infinite and boundless and illumines all things; where the light does not reach is called the shadow world of ignorance, the clusters and elements, the abode of all afflictions, which can harm people. The knowing mind is the light, errant thoughts are shadows; the light illumining things is called shining, and when the mind and thoughts do not range over things but are turned toward the original nature, this is called "turning the light around to shine back." It is also called "panoramic illumination"; illumining the whole of the immediate substance, it is where neither delusion nor enlightenment have ever appeared. Nowadays people think of basic mind by means of errant thoughts and consider afflictions enjoyable—when will they ever escape birth and death?

"The essence of sitting meditation is the nonproduction of a single thought; trying to stop thought by thought is like washing blood with blood—what should we do?"

The nonproduction of a single thought is what is known as the original essence of the mind. It is not stopping thought, yet it is also not not stopping thought; it is just the nonproduction of a single thought. If you merge with this original essence, this is called the realization of thusness of the reality of things. Thus, even sitting meditation is no use here—there is no illusion, no enlightenment, so how could there be thoughts? If you do not know this original essence, you cannot help but produce thoughts; even if you suppress them so they don't arise, this is all still ignorance. It is like a rock lying on the grass; before long the grass will grow again. You should work on meditation most meticulously and carefully; don't take it easy.

"Some say we should turn to the point where not a single thought is born; what about this?"

The nonproduction of a single thought is an expression referring to complete absence of any signs of birth, extinction, going, or coming. Birth and death come from the mind; if you don't know where thoughts come from, you cannot know the root of birth and death. Sentient beings are constantly afflicted by lustful, angry, foolish thoughts which compel them, making them turn away from their inherent nature. If the clouds of delusive thought clear, the moon of the nature of mind appears; the thoughts you hated before then becomes knowledge and wisdom, and you can use these thoughts to talk about reality and teach sentient beings. An ancient said, "You people are used by the twenty-four hours; I make use of the twenty-four hours."

"You say that when sitting in meditation, it is wrong when thoughts arise, yet wrong to stop them—so then what?"

Before you have seen reality, creating and stopping thoughts are both wrong; when it says in the Buddhist scriptures sometimes not to create false ideas, and sometimes it says not to cease and pass away, these are words to let us know of the fundamental reality. If you know fundamental reality, then cultivation of practice is not necessary; when the disease of illusion and delusion is removed, then there is no more use for cures. Even so, when the diseases of delusive feelings arise, then you need the cure of cultivation of practice. Thoughts arising is the disease; not continuing is the medicine.

"Even if thoughts arise, they have no reality of their own; what is wrong?"

Even though they have no reality of their own, as

soon as they arise you go wrong; it's like things in a dream—when you awaken you realize they were unreal; were you not mistaken? That which makes mistakes and produces dreams is sentient beings' false views; one day if they hear the teaching of enlightenment and are inspired with faith, this is much better. Even so, those who do not have a really genuine aspiration for enlightenment do not realize the errors of their minds because their application of effort is not careful; even though from time to time they suppress small thoughts, they are not aware of the big thoughts. If you do not cut off the root source, even if you have some affinity with the way, it will be impossible to escape birth and death.

"The sixth patriarch said, 'Do not think any good or bad at all.' To have no thoughts about good or bad surely is the essential point of sitting meditation; what are little thoughts and big thoughts?"

"Do not think any good or bad at all" are words that cut directly; not only in sitting meditation are they to be applied. If you reach this state, walking, standing, sitting, and lying down are all meditation; no need to cling to the form of sitting. A patriarch said, "Walking is also meditation; sitting is also meditation; speaking, silent, active or still, the body is peaceful." One of the Buddha's discourses says we are always in it, walking around, sitting, and lying down. Little thoughts are thoughts that suddenly arise about what is before you. Big thoughts are thoughts of things like greed, hatred, folly, false views, conceit, jealousy, name and fame, profit, and support. When sitting in meditation, those whose wills are weak may keep back little thoughts, but such evil thoughts as these [big ones] will remain unawares in their minds. These are called big thoughts. Giving up these big bad thoughts is called directly cutting off the root source; when you cut off the root source, afflictions become enlightenment, folly becomes wisdom, the three poisons become the three bodies of pure discipline, ignorance becomes the objective reality of great knowledge—need we speak of little thoughts? Buddha said, "If you can transform things, then they are the same as those who realize thusness." That's what this means. If you can transform things, don't be transformed by things.

" 'If you can transform things, you are the same as those who realize thusness'—what are things, what is transformation?"

Things are everything; transformation is complete liberation. Transforming things means that your mind is immutable in the midst of all things, turning back to fundamental nature, objects do not hinder the mind, heavenly demons, ghosts and spirits, afflictions, birth and death cannot overcome you. This is called transforming things. The essential point to watch is not to shift your mind onto things. Even views of Buddha and Dharma should be cut off, to say nothing of false thoughts; although the cutting mind seems like the thinking mind, this is right thought, and right thought is called wise thought. This is the knowledge and wisdom which enters into right seeing.

"It is clear that afflictions and enlightenment come from the mind, but just where do they begin?"

Seeing forms, hearing sounds, smelling odors, tasting flavors, sensing feelings, cognizing phenomena, are the functions of the powers of the six faculties; among these sense fields, that which distinguishes good and bad, discriminates false and true, is wisdom. Herein to set up others and self, producing love and hate, all are wrong views; development of attachment to forms based on these wrong views is called delusion, and from this delusion arise matter, sensation, perception, coordination, and consciousness—the five clusters—this is called affliction. Because sentient beings' physical bodies are built of afflictions, they indulge in murder, theft, adultery, falsehood, and other evil actions, and eventually degenerate into the three evil ways [hell fiends, hungry ghosts, animals]. All this comes from wrong thoughts; as soon as these wrong thoughts arise, if you can turn them right around toward fundamental reality, then you can attain mindlessness. Once you rest in no mind, then the five clusters become the five-element body of reality of those who come to realize thusness. This is called "abiding nowhere, yet activating the mind." Using your mind in this way is the great function of cultivation of practice.

"Someone who has long developed accomplishment at sitting meditation and whose work is pure and mature should not have any afflictions or delusion in his mind; how can those who are just beginning to cultivate practice put an end to afflictions?"

Don't despise afflictions, just purify your mind. An ancient said, "To study the way you must be made of iron; lay hold of the mind and it's settled. Directly approaching unexcelled enlightenment, don't worry about any right or wrong." Laying hold of the mind means judging if the mind is in a proper state or not; those who know their minds' errors are wise ones, and those with wisdom should not be deluded. It is like taking a lamp into a dark cave where sunlight or moonlight has never come in; the old darkness doesn't go outside, but suddenly it becomes light inside. With the light of wisdom, the darkness of ignorance and affliction don't have to go away to be gone. At night the sky is dark, but when the sunlight comes out, the sky becomes daylight. The mind is also like this; illusion is darkness, enlightenment is light—when the light of wisdom shines, the darkness of afflictions suddenly turns light. Enlightenment is not something separate.

"Illumining the darkness of afflictions depends on the light of wisdom; without wisdom there can be no enlightenment, so how can we attain this wisdom?"

Your own light of wisdom is clear and bright of itself, but when obscured by false ideas you lose this, and therefore create illusions. It is like when someone dreams; whatever it is seems to appear real, but after awakening there is not a single thing. Dreamlike illusions are seen to be originally nonexistent once you have awakened. Because sentient beings are deluded, they take the false for the true.

"If enlightenment means suddenly realizing something you didn't know before, then can one know things of the past and future?"

When false views are all ended and the great dream

suddenly wakes and you know the enlightened nature by seeing it, this is called great enlightenment, great penetration; such as this cannot be fathomed by discriminating thought. Knowing past and future events is a power of superknowledge and depends on effective power from cultivation and practice; it cannot be called great enlightenment. Heavenly devils, ghosts and spirits, outsiders and sorcerers all have supernormal powers, which are attributes attained by past practice of hardships and austerity. But although they have such attributes, they don't give up their false ideas and don't enter the way of the enlightened ones.

"If those who awaken to the way and realize the truth do not have supernormal powers, what useful qualities do they have?"

Because this mind is made of past follies and delusions, even in people who see reality and realize buddhahood, superpowers are not manifest. Even so, when enlightened, you transcend the fields of senses, cut off birth and death; so you naturally have superpowers and their inconceivable use, but these are not the powers of heavenly demons and outsiders, which have attachments. One who is vastly and greatly enlightened immediately realizes the way of the enlightened ones without passing through three immeasurable aeons; why specially talk about supernormal powers besides this?

"Is there any difference between 'seeing reality and realizing buddhahood' and 'this very mind is Buddha'?"

'This very mind is Buddha' indicates that there is no

Buddha outside of mind; one who can realize the meaning of this directly is sharp. This is also pointed out by the saying "not mind, not Buddha." Those who see reality and realize buddhahood know their own nature by direct seeing and cut off the root of life of sentience, clearly realize the perfect illumination of inconceivable real nature, so there is no birth and death, no afflictions—this is provisionally termed realizing buddhahood. Buddhahood is enlightenment, realizing you have never been deluded. Although there is no difference, it seems that there are differences among entry ways; that is why there are two expressions.

"If real nature is permanent and unchanging, the same in sentient beings as in buddhas, doesn't the fact that deluded sentient beings have the pains of birth and death mean that you can't say they are equal to buddhas?"

Equality is illumined by knowledge and wisdom, not seen by ignorant folly. The words and expressions of the ancestral teachers are tiles to knock on the door; when you have not yet entered the door, then the saying "seeing reality, fulfill buddhahood" is the ultimate. Once you have entered this door, you detach from all characteristics; so realizing buddhahood, too, involves no attainment.

"The exoteric and esoteric Buddhist schools all have guidelines; teaching, principle, knowledge, detachment, practice, station, cause, effect; disciples of the two vehicles cultivate the four stages of meditation and eight absorptions, are free from calamities caused by fire, water, and wind, empty matter, sensation, perception, coordination, and consciousness, and enter extinction without remainder. Bodhisattvas maintain three bodies of pure precepts, cultivate myriad practices out of great love and compassion, pass through the three stages of sagehood and ten ranks of holiness, cut off inner and outer afflictions. If where there are no afflictions is the sphere of buddhahood, why have the buddhas of the three times left the real world of true thusness and come to the realm of desire where there is birth and death?"

The buddhas and bodhisattvas make it their task to help sentient beings; if they do not help sentient beings, they are not buddhas or bodhisattvas—as long as those of the three vehicles do not help sentient beings, in the great vehicle this is called entering the deep pit of liberation. Bodhisattvas, in the three stages of sagehood and ten ranks of holy ones, cultivate practice and advance further into the multiplying hidden gates; in order to save sentient beings, they leave the blissful land of silent light and come to the miserable world of five corruptions to make trees of enlightenment. High meadows on dry ground do not produce lotuses; it is the mud of the low swamps that gives birth to lotus blossoms. A farmer who sows and reaps cannot plant crops on clear dry ground—putting dirty manure into wet mud, he plants rice seeds there, and with the proper basis and conditions, when the time comes and the sun's energy quickens them, sweet rain wets them, sprouts grow, roots and stems, branches and leaves flourish in profusion and grain ripens; when the farmer's work is done, he sing songs of peace and tranquillity. The appearance of the buddhas in the world is also like this; in the clear blue vastness of the sky, you cannot construct a teaching of enlightenment, so they put on dirty old ragged clothes in this defiled evil world of five corruptions to invite and guide sentient beings afflicted with evil doings by explaining the truth to them in accordance with their state and potential to understand, planting seeds of the true basis; when the time for the casual connections comes, the sun of wisdom shines, the breeze of compassion fans, the rain of truth refreshes, ambrosia descends, the sprouts of the way appear, the branches, leaves, roots, and stems flourish and grow, producing trees of enlightenment, causing flowers of perfect enlightenment to bloom and producing the fruit of inconceivable enlightenment, transforming and guiding, to perfect fulfillment, extolling the inconceivable state of eternal bliss of nirvana.

People of the way are like a tree blood body; putting the manure of the six sense fields on the ground, planting the seeds of living awareness, replanting the sprouts of physical bodies, sending forth shoots of inherent knowledge, producing the roots of mind and thoughts, growing the stems of conception and imagination, bringing forth branches of conscious spirit, sprouting leaves of emotions and desires, producing roots and trunk of pleasure, opening flowers of knowledge and vision, producing the fruit of enlightenment. When the work of the way is done, they sing the song of mindlessness.

Ordinary people are also like trees; on the thin soil of folly and delusion putting the manure of greed and lust, planting seeds of ignorance, transplanting shoots of the five clusters, producing buds of active habitual consciousness, growing roots of attachment and stems of the sense of others and self, bringing forth branches of flattery and deceit, sprouting leaves of jealousy and envy, creating trees of affliction, causing flowers of infatuation to bloom, forming fruits of the three poisons. When the tasks of fame and profit are done, they sing the songs of desires.

Now tell me: are these three kinds of trees any better or worse than each other? If there is anyone who can pull them out by the roots with a single hand and plant them on the ground where there is no light or shade and make a shadowless tree, he must be someone of great power, who has the same root as heaven and earth, the same body as myriad things. But tell me: who is this, what is he? If you say he is a Buddha, heaven and earth are far apart.

Sayings of National Teacher Shoitsu While Dwelling at Tofuku Zen Temple

• *Addressing the Community on the New Year*

Zen is not conception or perception; if you establish an idea, you turn away from the source. The way is beyond cultivated effects; if you set up accomplishment, you lose the essence. The news of the new year does not stir a bit of dust—harvesting blessings according to the season, no celebration inappropriate. If you assess it in terms of Buddhism, you are calling a bell a pitcher; if you call it mundane reality and its ordinary conventions, you fall on your face on level ground. Do you all understand? Early spring is still cold; return to the hall and have tea.

• *Offering Incense in Memory of Wujun*

In the old days when I was traveling, I sailed across seas and climbed mountains, dragging mud and dripping water, traveling all over the south. Then on Five Topknots Peak I bumped unawares into this old teacher [Wujun] and encountered his poison hand—there was no way for me to escape. Setting my eyebrows above my eyes, I cleared away my life and even up till now have nothing to explain, no principle to expound; now in the presence of the assembly I will raise the depths and turn them over—[raising the incense]

The rock of ages will someday wear away, but when will this sorrow end?

• *Address on the Occasion of a Buddha-Image-Washing Ceremony on Buddha's Birthday*

Prince Siddhartha, manifestation of the body of reality, today was born; in the palace of the King of Pure Food, nine dragons spit water to bathe the golden body, and golden lotuses sprouted from the ground to bear his feet. He boasted throughout heaven and earth, pointlessly opening his mouth and saying he alone was to be honored. He had all the adorning marks of a great man, and performed subtle and marvelous great Buddhist services. But what are great Buddhist services? [a silence] Getting down from the seat, asking the pillar and the lamp to enter the ocean of fragrant water of those who realize thusness, and help this old fellow turn the great wheel of the true teaching.

• *Informal Talk at the Beginning of Summer Retreat*

In the secret transmission on the Spiritual Mountain, the pure tradition of Shaolin, actions accord, words complement each other, great perfect awareness is one's own sanctuary. Body and mind dwelling at peace, with knowledge of equality of the real nature of all things, not going anywhere for ninety days, protecting creatures for three months, keeping pure as ice and snow. Summon forth great energy in your efforts, great courage and determination; wielding the sword of wisdom, go directly ahead, killing all, whether in the stage of learning or beyond learning, and after having killed all you see that mountains are mountains, rivers are rivers, the whole body comes thus, the whole body goes thus—there are no complications around at all. At this time, can you call it the fundamental business of a patch-robed monk? You must let go your hands over a mile-high precipice and appear with your whole body throughout the universe.

Tokusan said to his group, "According to my view, there are neither buddhas nor patriarchs. Bodhidharma was a greasy-smelling old barbarian; bodhisattvas of the tenth stage are dung haulers; the perfectly and inconceivably enlightened ones are immoral fools; enlightenment and nirvana are donkey-tethering stakes; the canonical teachings are ghost tablets, paper for wiping sores; the four grades of saints and three grades of sages, from initiates to those of the highest stages, are ghosts hanging around graves, unable to save even themselves." Tokusan can function beyond the crowd, clearly analyzing past and present, casting the all embracing net of the school to bring in latecomers. [raising his staff] Even so, his nose has been pierced by this staff of mine so that he has no way to breathe. Is there anyone in the crowd who can show some energy? [planting his staff once] Those with eyes discern.

• *Address at the Beginning of Summer Retreat*

Going high beyond the ten stages of bodhisattvahood without going through countless eons of practice, things and self one thusness, mind and body equanimous, not keeping company with myriad things, not on the same road as the thousand saints; this is bringing forth the whole potential of buddhas and patriarchs, alone revealing the true eye of humans and gods, just dwelling on the summit of the solitary peak, forbidden to leave, yet extending your hands at the crossroads, killing and giving life freely, capturing and releasing freely. But tell me: is there anything in this that is in accord with the holy precepts? [a silence] No interchange in daily activities, right in your being there is shutting down and opening up.

• *Informal Talk at the End of Summer Retreat*

The great potential and great function, free in all ways, not lingering in the sages' barriers of potential, not falling into the nest of the patriarchs, clean and naked, with no defilement, bare and unhindered, with nothing concealed—the original face, the scene of the fundamental ground, speaking without sound, shattered along with the words, not anything before form, merging together with things, opening the cloth bag, smashing the iron gate barrier, wielding the blown-hair sword, coming from the south going north, your state thoroughly peaceful, treading on reality with every step. But tell me: what is the expression of walking on reality? If you don't enjoy the purity of ice, how can you appreciate the purity of snow?

Instructions of National Teacher Shoitsu

• *To Eminent Kumyo*

In the direct teachings of the ancestral masters, there are no special techniques, just to lay down all entanglements, put to rest all concerns, and watch the tip of your nose for six hours in the daytime and six hours at night; whenever you wander into distinctions among things, just raise a saying—don't think of it in terms of the way to enlightenment, don't think of it in terms of purification, don't consciously anticipate understanding, don't let feelings create doubt or despair, but go directly in like cutting through an iron bun with a single stroke, where there is no flavor, no path of reason, without getting involved in other thoughts. After a long time, you will naturally be like waking from a dream, like a lotus blossom opening. At this moment, the saying you have been observing is just a piece of tile to knock at the door—throw it over on the other side and then look instead at the sayings of the enlightened ancestors and buddhas expressing activity in the world of differentiation. All of these are just to stop children crying; the one road going beyond does not let a single thread through, but cuts off the essential crossing between ordinary and holy, while students toil over forms like monkeys grasping at the moon. We might say that if you forget your own body and go frantically searching outside, when can you ever find it? Sitting peacefully on a cushion, day and night seeking to become buddhas, rejecting life and death in hopes of realizing enlightenment, is all like the monkey's grasping at the moon. If you want some real help, it's just that not minding is the way; yet it's not the same as wood or stone—always aware and knowing, perfectly distinctly clear, seeing and hearing are normal; there are no further details.

Elder Kumyo sits facing a wall day and night and has asked for some words to urge him on. Not begrudging the way of my house, I have let my brush write this, 1267.

• *To Elder Nyo*

Buddha after buddha extended their hands, not only for others; it was of their own power of gratitude. A square peg fitting into a round hole, a clod of earth washed in the mud, communicated patriarch to patriarch, an empty valley answering a voice, calling south north, three ways across and four ways up, sitting one and walking seven, difficulty and confusion is unavoidable. In the dark dim semiawakeness before a single breath has appeared, if you can trust completely, you are still in the secondary—if you don't get it until the indiscernible is already distinguished, you have fallen into the third level.

See for yourself. Directly transcend the principles and activities of the buddhas and patriarchs, go through the forest of thorns, transcend the barriers of potential described by the ancestral teachers, pass through the silver mountain and iron wall—then for the first time you will realize there is a transcendent fundamental endowment; you can sit and wear clothes, helping people solve their sticking points and untie their bonds.

Elder Nyo has been in the assembly for years and now returns to his native place. He wouldn't turn back even if called; he cannot be trapped or held. He returns barefoot. So I write this to send him off.

• *To Eminent Chizen*

In the school of the ancestral teachers we point directly to the human mind; verbal explanations and illustrative devices actually miss the point. Not falling into seeing and hearing, not following sound or form, acting freely in the phenomenal world, sitting and lying in the heap of myriad forms, not involved with phenomena in breathing out, not bound to the clusters and elements of existence in breathing in, the whole world is the gate of liberation, all worlds are true reality. A universal master knows what it comes to the moment it is raised; how will beginners and latecomers come to grips with it? If you don't get it yet, for the time being we open up a pathway in the gateway of the secondary truth, speak out where there is nothing to say, manifest form in the midst of formlessness. How do we speak where there is nothing to say? "A mortar runs through the sky." How do we manifest form from formlessness? "The west river sports with a lion."

During your daily activities responding to circumstances in the realm of distinctions, don't think of getting rid of anything, don't understand it as a hidden marvel—with no road of reason, no flavor, day and night, forgetting sleep and food, keep those sayings in mind.

If you still don't get it, we go on to speak of the tertiary, expounding mind and nature, speaking of mystery and marvel; one atom contains the cosmos, one thought pervades everywhere. Thus an ancient said:

Infinite lands and worlds
With no distinctions between self and others
Ten ages past and present
Are never apart from this moment of thought

Chizen brought some paper seeking some words, so I dashed this off, senile and careless; after looking at it once, consign it to the fire.

• *To Zen Man Chimoku*

Since the buddhas and patriarchs, there have been three general levels of dealing with people. On the uppermost level there are no further techniques, no meaning of principle; verbal understanding is impossible. If you can take it up directly at this, then there is no difference from "the cypress in the garden," "three pounds of hemp," "swallow the water of the west river in one gulp."

On the second level, it is just a matter of bringing

out a question, going along to break through; this is like Rinzai questioning Obaku and getting hit sixty times.

On the third level, we enter the mud and water, setting down footnotes, blinding people's eyes, destroying the lineage of the Buddha.

But a true patch-robed one must search out and investigate the living word, not go for the dead word. Eminent Chimoku, you are pure and true; if you can attain realization at the living word, you can be teacher of buddhas and patriarchs. Not begrudging my family way, I have shown you three levels of device.

• *To Elder Kakujitsu*

The fundamental style of the ancestral teachers, the one expression of transcendence, plunging into the other side with a heroic spirit, then being free wherever you are, inconceivable activities unhindered. Wielding the jewel sword of the diamond king, cutting off difficulty and confusion, using the killing and reviving staff to eliminate affirmation and denial. Striking and shouting at appropriate times, sitting one walking seven; by this that tawny-faced old teacher Shakyamuni assembled all kinds of people over three hundred and sixty times—able to act as king of the teaching, he was free in all respects. The blue-eyed first patriarch sat for nine years facing a wall and offered instruction for later students—"outwardly ceasing all involvements, inwardly no sighing in the mind, mind like a wall, thereby one may enter the way." These and their like are elementary techniques; later you realize on your own—casting off all involvements, letting myriad things rest, is the foremost technique. If you stick to this technique, then it is not right. It cannot be helped, to give meticulous explanations, to mix with the mud and water, to use a stake to extract a stake, to use a state to take away a state; a thousand changes, myriad transformations, seven ways up and down, eight ways across. If you take the words as the rule, you will produce interpretations along with the words and fall into the clusters and elements of physical-mental existence, the world of shadows; if you don't even know techniques, how could you know the true source?

Elder Kakujitsu is extraordinary by nature, a completely pure person. He asked for some words of exhortation, so I wrote this.

• *To a Zen Man*

On the forehead, at the feet, it is necessary to realize here is a great road through the heavens. Without establishing the practice and vows of Samantabhadra or speaking of the active knowledge of Manjusri, hold Vairocana still so that all traces of ordinary or holy disappear—then afterward the great capacity and great function will come into being wherever you may be; on the hundred grasses speaking of the provisional and the true, in the heap of sound and form setting up illumination and function, giving helpful techniques, freely and independently. But if you have a clear-eyed person look at this, it is still only halfway—it is still wearing stocks presenting evidence of your crime.

However, even so, you must know there are methods of offering help and guidance; one is the technique of sitting meditation, the other is the technique of direct pointing. Sitting meditation is the great calm; direct pointing is the great wisdom. Before the empty eon, on the other side of the ancient buddhas, self-enlightenment without a teacher, without any such techniques—this is what Bodhidharma taught, the hidden transmission of personal experience. After the empty eon, there is enlightenment and delusion, there are questions and answers, there are teachers and students; all these are guiding techniques.

The buddhas have come forth, with "merging of inner reality," "barriers of potential," "transcendence," "reintegration," "coming from light, merging in darkness," "sun face Buddha, moon face Buddha,"—taking in the hand a talisman that lights the night, wielding the diamond sword with the eye of an adept, using tongs and hammer in accord with the situation, not needing verbal explanations, not needing devices or objectives, those of superior knowledge with sharp faculties penetrate through to direct realization; they can be said to be like the sky covering all, like the earth supporting all; vast and open as empty space, shining in all directions, like sun and moon. An ancient said, "In the community of the fifth patriarch, seven hundred eminent monks all understood Buddhism. There was only workman Lu who didn't understand Buddhism." This is the way of direct pointing; as for the technique of sitting meditation, you are already thoroughly familiar with this and don't need my instruction. As you come with some paper asking for a saying, I scribble this senile confusion.

Awakening on your own without a teacher before the empty eon and being awakened by a teacher after the appearance of the buddhas and patriarchs, that is awakening and being awakened, are both techniques of guidance. All that has been communicated from buddhas to patriarchs, inconceivable liberated activity, is all just the mutual accord of states and words.

Great Master Bodhidharma crossed the sea and crossed the river, sat upright for nine years facing a wall, and returned alone with one shoe—this, too, was in the sphere of accord of words and actions. Eminent, if you want to attain accord, you must cut off the root of birth and death, break up the nest of sage and sainthood, become clean and naked, bare and untrammeled, not relying on anything; only then will you have some realization. Now when I speak this way, is there any accord? Is there none? If you can search it out, don't say I didn't tell you.

Sayings of National Teacher Daio at Kofuku Zen Temple

• *Informal Talk at the Beginning of Winter*

Everything is the original law; every day the morning sun clears the sky, in every mind there is no separate mind, in every place the pure wind circles the earth. If you can understand immediately in this way, then there is no need for Shakyamuni to appear in the world or for Bodhidharma to come from the west—in everyone it towers like a mile-high wall, flashing a great precious light in everyone's presence. One thought ten thousand years, ten thousand years one thought, eating when hungry, sleeping when tired, who worries about the alternation of light and dark, the change of seasons? Who talks about ice forming from each drop of water, who says when the weather is cold the people are cold? Even if you go on this way, this is still ordinary behavior; how can ultimate transcendence be revealed? [hitting with his whisk] If winter isn't cold, wait and see after the twelfth month.

An ancient worthy said, "If you want to know the meaning of enlightened nature, you must watch the causal relations of time and season; when the time has arrived, the truth is manifest of itself." Now it is the beginning of the winter season; tell me, what is the truth that is revealed? [striking with his whisk] When one sun rises, myriad species are born.

• *Address in the Teaching Hall*

A monk asked Joshu, "What is the path?"

Joshu said, "The one beyond the fence."

The monk said, "I'm not asking about that path."

Joshu said, "What path are you asking about?"

The monk said, "The great path."

Joshu said, "The great path goes to the capital."

Daio said in verse: "He points it out so clearly, face to face without deception; the great path is straight as a bowstring, but travelers make trouble for themselves."

• *Informal Talk on New Year's Eve*

Hanging high the jewel mirror, ranging myriad images before the eyes, holding the sharp sword sideways, cutting off all impulses beyond conception, covering heaven and earth, passing through form and sound, shutting down and opening up at will, killing and giving life according to the occasion, in full command of holding fast or letting go. This is whereby patch-robed monks explain what cannot be practiced and practice what cannot be explained, changing in thousands of ways freely—even disrupting the order of time and wiping out the elemental spirits is not beyond their capability. But even so, tonight I forgo the first move; when the twelfth month is over, as of old, it is up to spring to return. Why? I want you people to take care at all times.

• *Address in the Teaching Hall on the First Night of the New Year*

[describing a circle in the air with his whisk] Lighting this lamp, all lamps immediately shine; the dense web of myriad shapes and forms has nowhere to hide. If under an overturned bowl, how can you blame me? [a long silence] But tell me: what lamp is it?

• *Address in the Teaching Hall on the Anniversary of Buddha's Demise*

The single heart not dwelling in extinction pointlessly sells off the golden body; up till now the ugliness has been impossible to conceal—what a mess, every year, the peach-blossom spring.

• *Address in the Teaching Hall on the First Day of March*

Speaking of Zen, expounding the way, talking about marvel and mystery, is all gouging wounds in healthy flesh. Ultimately, what? "I always remember southern

China in the spring, the fragrance of the hundred flowers as the partridges cry."

• *Address in the Teaching Hall*

Great Master Ummon said to his group, "Monks, don't think falsely; mountains are mountains, rivers are rivers."

Then a monk came forward and said, "How is it when I see that mountains are mountains and rivers are rivers?"

Ummon said, "Why is the Buddha shrine passing through here?"

The monk said, "Then I am not thinking falsely."

Ummon said, "Give me back the words."

[citing this, Daio said] So then what is easy to open is the beginning and ending mouth; what is difficult to maintain is the heart of the dead of winter. When that monk heard Ummon say, "Why is the Buddha shrine passing through here?" if he had just said, "It should be so," he would not only have shown his own light, he would have also seen through Ummon's standpoint.

• *Address on the Anniversary of Buddha's Mahaparinirvana*

The Buddha body fills the cosmos, manifest to all sentient beings everywhere. [raising his whisk] This a whisk; where is the Buddha body? People, if you can set a single eye here, you will see the solemn assembly on Spiritual Mountain has not yet dispersed, but if you hesitate and doubt, the ancient Buddha is long gone.

National Teacher Daio's Letters to Meditators

• *To Zen Man Gentei*

The World Honored One raised a flower, Kasyapa smiled—gold is not exchanged for gold, water does not wash water; since then it has come down from generation to generation, taking in an echo from empty space, one person communicating it to one other. Hence we see Zen teachers doing things like going east to west, west to east, Hoshan beating a drum, Bimo raising his forked stick, Xuefeng rolling balls, Judi raising his finger, three pounds of hemp, the cypress tree in the garden, and myriad other illustrations, hundreds of thousands of actions using it, all coming forth in the same pattern, strung through on one thread. If one is a genuine patch-robed monk, who would care whose ladle handle was long or short? If you don't dump the gourd, the vinegar becomes sharper and sharper. Just go by your own sight; live on your own. Eminent Gentei, quickly set your eyes to see before the World Honored One raised the flower; keep watching whatever you do until this work becomes pure and refined to the point where in one moment you merge and see the original face, the scenery of the original ground. At that time, tawny old Buddha and the golden ascetic Kasyapa will both stand downwind of you. That is why it is said that a powerful man is the ancestor of mind before heaven and earth. Think of this, eminent Tei, think of this.

• *To Kyoen, Latter Abbot of Manju Monastery*

When Rinzai left Obaku long ago, Obaku said, "Where are you going?" Rinzai said, "If not south of the river, then north of the river." Obaku then hit him. Rinzai grabbed the staff and slapped him. Obaku laughed loudly, called his attendant, and said, "Bring me the meditation brace and whisk of my late master Hyakujo."

Rinzai called to the attendant, "Bring me fire." After all, a good son doesn't use his father's money.

Obaku said, "Just take them away; later you will cut off the tongue of everyone on earth." This old fellow cared so for his child that he did not mind being unseemly.

Eminent Kyoen has been with us on this mountain for four years, and his determination and mindfulness in investigation of the way are solid and firm; in his daily actions he is never off balance. Now he is going to another mountain and has come to take leave of us. Though the eminent has the ability to ask for fire, I have no meditation brace or whisk to hand over. But tell me: is this the same as the ancients or different? If you should encounter someone at a crossroads in a village of three families, don't misquote this.

• *To Nun Gentai*

Sister Gentai, from the capital. Her determination in seeking the way is keen, and she often comes to inquire further into the basis and conditions of this great matter. One day I said to her, "At the top of the hundred-foot pole, go forward."

She said, "At the top of the hundred-foot pole, there is no place to go."

I said, "Where there is no place to step, go a hundred thousand steps farther—only then will you be able to walk alone in the red skies, pervading the universe as your whole body." She agreed and smiled; that's all. Although she has not yet gotten the gist of it, she is not the same as ordinary folk who get stuck on even ground.

Now you want to return to your old capital and have come with incense in your sleeve to ask for a saying. I once made a verse of praise on the master of Ikusan in Daryo,* so I will write that:

* The master of Ikusan worked on a koan—"How to proceed forward from atop the hundred-foot pole? Uh!"—for three years, when one day, as he was crossing a valley stream on a donkey, the bridge plank broke and he fell, whereupon he was greatly enlightened. Atop the pole means at the peak of meditation, or personal detachment and liberation, or it can be used to refer to the farthest point of any aspect of work on the way. It usually refers, however, to the esoteric death, after which the "step forward," return to life, at one with the world, is the beginning of the next, usually more difficult, phase of Zen study.

Atop the pole, walk on by the ordinary route—
It is most painful, when taking a tumble in a valley
Earth, mountains, and rivers cannot hold you up
And space suppresses laughter, filling a donkey's cheeks

I ask you, Zen nun, to bring this up and look at it time and again; how to go forward from atop the pole? Suddenly, when the time comes, you can go forward a step, and space will surely swallow a laugh. Remember, remember.

• *To Bath Steward Genan*

The peak experience, the final act; as soon as you try to pursue it in thought, there are white clouds for a thousand miles. But even if you go back upon seeing the monastery flagpole at a distance, or head off freely upon seeing a beckoning hand, this is still only half the issue; it is not yet the strategic action of the whole capability.

Bath steward An has traveled and studied various places and spent a long time in monasteries. Don't stick to the ruts in the road of the ancients—you must travel a living road on your own. East, west, foot up, foot down, using it directly—only then will you know the peak experience illumines the heavens and covers the earth, illumines the past and flashes through the present. This is your own place to settle and live. When I say this, I am only using water to offer flowers, never adding anything extra. This of this, eminent, think of this.

• *To Zen Man Kusho*

The cause and conditions of the one great concern of the enlightened ones is not apart from your daily affairs; there is no difference between here and there—it pervades past and present, shining through the heavens mirroring the earth. That is why it is said that everything in the last myriad eons is right in the present. We value the great spirit of a hero only in those concerned—before any signs become distinct, before any illustration is evident, concentrate fiercely, looking, looking, coming or going, till your effort is completely ripe and in the moment of a thought you attain union, the mind of birth and death is destroyed and suddenly you clearly see your original appearance, the scene of your native land; each particular distinctly clear, you then see and hear just as the buddhas did, know and act as the enlightened ancestors did. Only then do you really manage to avoid defeat in your original purpose of leaving home and society and traveling for knowledge and enlightenment. Zen man Kusho, work on this.

• *To Zen Man Genchu*

Since ancient times, the enlightened ancestors appearing in the world relied just on their own fundamental experience to reveal something of what is before us; so we see them knocking chairs and raising whisks, hitting the ground and brandishing sticks, beating a drum or rolling balls, hauling dirt and stones—"A ten-ton catapult is not shot at a rat."

Even though this is so, eminent Genchu, you have traveled all over and spent a long time in monasteries; don't worry about such old calendar days as these I mentioned—just go by the living road you see on your own; going east, going west, like a hawk sailing through the skies. In the blink of an eye you cross over to the other side.

If you are not yet capable of this, then look directly at before the enlightened ones were present, before the world was differentiated; twenty-four hours a day, walking, standing, sitting, reclining, carefully, continuously, closely, minutely, look, look, all the time. When this directed effort becomes fully developed and pure, suddenly in an instant you are united, the routine mind is shattered and you see the fundamental countenance, the scenery of the basic ground. Everything will be distinctly clear; it is as if ten suns were shining. When you get to this state, you should be even more careful and thorough going. Why? At the last word you finally reach the impenetrable barrier.

Eminent Genchu has been with our group for a summer and suddenly wants to go to another mountain. Just before leaving, he asked for some words, so I wrote this, letting the pen write what it would, to fulfill his request.

Praises of Kannon by Daio

the sphere of perfect communion is clear everywhere
the pitcher water is alive, the willow eyes are green
there are also cold crags and early green bamboo
why are people these days in such a great hurry?

the cliffs are high and deep, the waters rush and tumble
the realm of perfect communion is new in each place
face to face, the people who meet her don't recognize her
when will they ever be free from the harbor of illusion?

lotus blossoms always in her hands, she stands alone
    magnificent
a boy comes to call
wordless, eyes resemble eyebrows
know that outside of joining the palms and bowing the head
how could this thing be explained to him?

the sound of the rushing spring is cool and subtle
the colors of the mountain crags are deep but distinct
in every field the realm of perfect communion
how can Sudhana know?

the dense crags jut forth precipitous
the waterfalls spew an azure loom
in each land the sphere of perfect communion
those who go right in are rare

the clouds are thin, the river endless
the universal door appears without deception
questioning the boy, he doesn't yet know it exists
he went uselessly searching in the cold of the mist and waves
in a hundred cities

Notes from Jakushitsu

• *To Wayfarer Zentatsu*

The sixth patriarch of Zen in China, in replying to a question from a government inspector, Mr. I, said, "Deluded people invoke a buddha's name seeking to be reborn in that buddha's land, but enlightened people purify their own minds. That is why the Buddha said that as the mind is pure, so is the Buddha land pure. Mr. inspector, you are a man of the East; as long as your mind is pure, you are faultless. Even people of the West [in the direction of paradise], if their minds are not pure, still have something wrong with them. When people of the East commit crimes, they invoke Amitabha Buddha's name seeking to be reborn in western paradise; when people of the West commit crimes, what land should they seek to be born in by invoking Buddha's name? The ignorant don't comprehend their own nature and do not recognize the pure land within their bodies, but wish for the West, for the East" and so on.

Essentially invoking of Buddha names is for liberation from birth and death; investigation of Zen is for realizing the nature of mind. We have never heard of anyone who awakened to the nature of mind who was not liberated from birth and death; how could someone freed from birth and death misunderstand the nature of mind? It should be realized that Buddha name remembrance and investigation of Zen have different names but are essentially the same.

Nevertheless, as an ancient said, "The slightest

entanglement of thought is the basis of the most miserable types of behavior; if feelings arise for a moment, they lock you up for ten thousand eons." So even Buddha name remembrance is producing dust on a mirror, even investigating Zen is putting rubbish in the eye. If you can just trust completely in this way, then you will not be deceived.

Wayfarer Zentatsu has diligently practiced concentration on Buddha name remembrance for years, and has suddenly come to my house asking for a robe and bowl, and to receive the great precepts; as he needs some admonitions for his daily life, so I hurriedly wrote this and gave it to him.

• *To Blind Tsumei*

In ancient times Aniruddha used to indulge in sleeping, so the Buddha scolded him, "You're like a clam." So he didn't sleep for seven days and awakened the power of clairvoyance, whereby he could see the whole universe like looking at a fruit in his hand.

If you have real will regarding the great matter of birth and death, you should take the koan "mind itself is Buddha" and bring it up time and again to awaken you, summoning it up wherever you are. One morning you will suddenly break through the lacquer bucket of ignorance—this is called "having the eye of the truth on your forehead." At that time will you fly around seeing the worlds of the universe? Hundreds of millions of polar mountains, infinite Buddha fields, you see on the tip of a hair—there is nothing else. This is my ultimate bequest to you.

• *To Wayfarer Ryosei*

A monk asked great master Baso, "What is Buddha?"

Baso said, "The mind itself is Buddha."

That monk was greatly enlightened at these words. It seems that what is so close that it is hard to see is the mind, and what is so far and yet easy to approach is buddhahood. If you misunderstand your mind, you are an ordinary man; if you realize your mind, you are a sage. There is no difference at all whether man, woman, old, young, wise, foolish, human, animal, whatever. Thus, in the Lotus of Truth assembly, was it not the eight-year-old Naga girl who went directly south to the undefiled world Amala, sat on a jewel lotus flower, and realized universal complete enlightenment?

In ancient times, master Ganto once was a boatman. A woman came with a child in her arms and asked, "I don't ask about plying the pole and rudder—what about the child in this woman's arms, where does it come from?" Ganto immediately hit her once. The woman said, "I have nursed seven children; six did not meet a real knower, and this one can't appreciate it." Then she threw the child in the river. This woman found out the way that mind itself is Buddha.

Skeletons
by
Zen Master
Ikkyu

It is in the written word that all things can be seen together.

In the beginning of mental evolution, one should concentrate on sitting meditation.

Whatever is born in any land all becomes naught.

One's own body is not primary; not even the original face of sky and earth and all nations and lands is primary—all come from emptiness. Because it has no form, it is called Buddha, enlightened. Various names such as enlightened mind, mental buddha, mind of reality, buddhas, enlightened ancestors, spiritized ones—all come from this. Unless you realize this, you're going right to hell.

Also, according to the teaching of good people, we do not return after going separate ways into the lands of darkness; those who are close and those who are inconstant both revolve in the flow of the three realms—feeling ever more weary of this, I left my native village, going nowhere in particular.

Coming to an unfamiliar abandoned temple, even as I wrung out my sleeves, I realized it was already nightfall. With no way to get together even a grass pillow for a nap, as I looked around here and there, there were mossy graves at a distance from the path, near the foot of the mountain, where the fields of meditation were sparse. One especially miserable-looking skeleton came out from behind the hall and said:

The autumn wind has risen in the world,
in the fields and mountains where you'll go
when the fall flowers beckon.

What can be done for the body,
as a black-dyed sleeve
in the heart of a man who wastes it? [1]

Everyone must sometime become naught. Becoming naught is called "returning to the fundamental." When you sit facing a wall, the thoughts which arise from conditioning are all unreal. The Buddha's fifty years of teachings are not real either. It's just to know people's minds.

Wondering if there were anyone who understands this suffering, I went into the hall and spent the night there, even lonelier than usual, unable to sleep.

Around dawn, as I dozed off a bit, in a dream I went out behind the hall, and saw a crowd of skeletons all acting in different ways, just like people in the world. As I watched with a sense of wonder, some skeletons came up and said:

When it passes
without a memory,
this worthless body
becomes a dream.

If you divide the way of enlightenment
into buddhas and kami,
how can you enter the true path? [2]

As long as it travels the road of life
in the present for a while,
the corpse in the fields
seems elsewhere.[3]

Anyway, as I got familiar with them and relaxed, the feeling I'd had of separation between myself and others disappeared. What's more, my skeleton companions wanted to give up the world and seek the truth; seeking separation from excess, going from shallow to deep—in searching out the source of one's own mind, what fills the ears is the sound of wind in the pines, what blocks the eyes is left on the pillow under the moon.

When are we not in a dream, when are we not skeletons, after all? Male and female forms exist only as long as these skeletons are wrapped up and put to use inside five-tone flesh; when life ends and the body bag breaks, there are no such forms—neither are high or low distinguished. Under the flesh which you now care for and enjoy, this skeleton is wrapped up and set in motion; you should acquiesce to this idea—in this there is no difference between high and low, old and young. Only when you awaken to the condition of the one great matter will you know the imperishable truth.

If a stone is good enough
for an effigy after death,
hang a scrap of writing
on a monument of five elements—

What is it? Oh! A frightening figure of a man!

While you have the single cloudless moon
how have you come to the darkness
of the fleeting world?

You must think it true; when the breath stops and the skin of the body comes apart, everyone turns out like this—your body cannot live forever.

A sign of how long is your time
are the pines of Sumiyoshi
planted before.

Give up the mind that thinks there is a self; just go with the wind driving the floating cloud of the body, and come this way. You want to live indefinitely, to the same age; you would really think so—this is the same frame of mind.

Since the world is a sleepless dream,
in vain do people start awake
upon seeing this.

It is useless to pray for a definite lifespan. You shouldn't keep anything on your mind except the One

Great Matter. Since life in the human world is uncertain, it is not a matter of awakening to this just now for the first time. Since it is a way to become detached, the sorrow of the world is quite happy.

Why adorn a mere temporary form?
Didn't you know it had to be [temporary] like this?

The original body must return
to the original place;
don't seek out where you won't go.

Nobody understands life;
there is no dwelling place—
when you return, you must become
the original earth.

Although there are many paths
up the base of the mountain,
we see the same moon on the high peak.

Since where you are going
you don't establish a home there,
there's not even a road to get lost on.

Having no beginning or end,
one's mind should not be thought of
as being born, or dying.

Left to do as it will,
the mind doesn't even think things through—
better to have controlled it
and given up the world.

Rain, sleet, snow, ice—
as such they may be different,
but when melted they're the same valley stream
water.

Although the path of the liberated mind may change,
behold the same law
of the cloud dweller.[4]

A straight path buried under the fallen pine needles;
hardly do we realize it is a house where people dwell.

How hopeless, the trip to the funeral pyre—[5]
as the fallen, they must stay.
[Is it transitory, the trip to the burning pyre?
as the fallen, they must stay.]

Tired of the world,
how long will you see the evening smoke of the pyre
as another's sorrow?

How fleeting, the faces of the people
whom we saw only yesterday,
as they vanish into the smoky evening.

So sad, the evening smoke of the funeral pyres;
only the sky is left behind by the wind,
as it was before.

Of what becomes ash when burnt, earth when buried,
what could be left as sin?

The sins committed up till the age of three
all disappear together,
as does eventually the self.

This must be what is certain in the world. Thinking how vain are those who do not realize that even today, right now, there must be such helplessness and death, and are startled by it, if asked how their lives should be, some say that these days, unlike the past, they are leaving the temples. In olden times, those who aspired to the way would enter a monastery, but nowadays they are all leaving the monasteries.

When you look at them, the monks have no knowledge, they don't like to sit and meditate; without making any efforts, they admire utensils, adorn cushions—full of conceit, they make their reputation just by wearing the robe, but even wearing the robe of monkhood, they are surely just lay people in disguise. Even though they wear the robe and surplice, the robe becomes a rope tying them up, and the surplice becomes an iron rod thrashing them, so it seems.

If we look carefully into the meaning of the cycles of birth and death, destroying life leads to hell, by greed we become hungry ghosts, by ignorance we become animals, by anger we become titans; by maintaining the five precepts [6] we are born human, and by carrying out the ten virtues [7] we are born divine. Above these states are the four holy ones [8]—added all together, they make ten realms.

Looking at this single moment of thought,[9] it has no shape, it abides nowhere for its duration, and there is nothing in it to despise and reject. It is like clouds in the vast sky, like bubbles on the water. Just because there are no thoughts arising, there is nothing to do either. Thoughts and things are one emptiness. I don't know about people's doubts.

People's parents are like striking fire: the steel is the father; the flint is the mother; the spark is the child. Setting this to a wick, when the sustenance of fuel and oil is exhausted, the fire goes out. When the father and mother make love, that is like the fire coming forth; since father and mother have no beginning, eventually they fade away in the mind where the fire has gone out. Openly embracing all things through emptiness, all forms are produced. When you let go of all forms, this is called the basic ground. All forms—of plants, trees, and land—all come from emptiness, so as a temporary metaphor it is called the fundamental ground.

When you break up a cherry tree and look,
there are no flowers at all;
the flowers are brought by the spring wind.

Even though you soar boundlessly
even beyond the clouds,
just don't rely on
the teachings of Gautama.

If, hearing the teachings spoken by Gautama over fifty years, you want to try to put the teachings into practice, what Gautama said at the end was that from the beginning to the end he had not said a single word; instead, he raised a flower in his hand, whereat Kasyapa smiled faintly. Then Gautama said, "I have the straightforward heart of the true teaching," and put down the flower. If you wonder what it means, Gautama said, in effect, "What I have been teaching for some fifty years is like when you're cuddling a baby pretending to be holding something in your hand; my fifty-odd years of teaching was like this call to Kasyapa."

Therefore the teachings which he transmitted were like the cuddling of the baby. But this flower cannot be known by means of the body, nor is it the mind; even speaking of it, you cannot know it. You should understand this body and mind thoroughly. Even if you are called a knowledgeable person, you cannot [therefore] be called a Buddhist. As for this flower, the teaching of the one vehicle of all the buddhas of past, present, and future appearing in the world refers to this flower. From the twenty-eight patriarchs in India and six patriarchs in China up till now, there has never been anything but the fundamental ground. Because everything is beginningless, it is called great; all modes of consciousness are produced from emptiness.

Even the summer, fall, and winter of the flowers of spring, the colors of the plants and trees, also are made from emptiness.

Also, the so-called four gross elements are earth, water, fire, and air. People hardly know what these are. Breath is air, warmth is fire, body fluid is water; if you burn or bury this, it becomes earth. There, too, because there is no beginning, nothing remains at all.

Whatever it is
is nothing but the world of delusion
since even "death" does not turn out
to be a real vacation.

Everybody, everybody, in the eyes of illusion though the body dies the spirit does not die—this is a great mistake. In the language of the enlightened, they say that the body and the seed die as one. Even "Buddha" means emptiness. You should return to the basic ground of sky, earth, land, and everything.

Giving up the eighty thousand teachings of all the scriptures, just understand this all rolled into one. You will become people of great peace and happiness.

Even written down,
they're just marks made in a dream;
after waking up, there is no one else who asks.

4/8/1457 Ikkyu-shi Sojun, seventh generation after Xutang, in Daitoku Temple before the eastern sea.

Notes to Ikkyu's *Skeletons*

1. The black-dyed sleeve symbolizes renunciation, as the robe of the homeless. A verse of Saint Ippen (1239–1289), a pure land sage of earlier Japan, says, "Giving up the body as well as the idea of giving up, an unthinking black-dyed sleeve in the world." Contained in homonymy and association is the sense "You should live in the world after renunciation, giving up even the idea 'I abandon.'" This is why Ikkyu still warns against wasting it.
2. Kami are nature spirits associated with Japanese earth and life consciousness; they were thought to protect, accept, and uphold Buddhist teachings. The aforementioned Saint Ippen received his major revelations through the mediumship of kami, and later taught the fundamental meaning of prayer underlying all forms of respect. Many eminent Buddhist teachers also preached the nonduality of the spirit and Buddha ways.
3. The corpse in the fields that seems elsewhere is the living body. A verse of Saint Ippen says: "Is it meaningless? While the corpse has not yet decayed, the meadow earth seemed to be elsewhere." This he spoke at the ruins of his grandfather's grave.
4. The law of the cloud dweller is impermanence; in ancient texts it is sometimes used for absolute transcendence or absolute indifference—we might say, death, as the most personal and cutting expression of impermanence. The great Zen master Hakuin wrote that one who sees into death is safe.
5. The Japanese uses the name of a mountain where bodies were taken to be burned. The variant English reading in parentheses is to highlight the allusion to the sense of the permanence of impermanence.

6. The five precepts are not to kill on purpose; not to steal in any way, even indirectly; not to be greedy or overindulgent in the course of human life; not to drink or sell liquor; and not to lie.
7. "Ten virtues" can have several references. Commonly they refer to the preceding five moral precepts, plus not talking about people's faults, not praising yourself and degrading others, not being stingy or predatory, not being angry without shame, and not repudiating the three treasures of the enlightened ones, their teaching and their communities. In the most ancient teachings, it is said that the Buddha had monks restrain useless mundane talk, but rather discourse on the merits and virtues of ten things: effort, little desire and being content, bravery, learning and the ability to explain the teaching to others, being fearless and unawed, being impeccable in conduct, being accomplished in meditation, wisdom and knowledge, liberation, and the vision and knowledge of liberation. In the esoteric teachings, in which terms Ikkyu sometimes wrote, there are two explanations: one is not regressing from the determination for enlightenment; not abandoning the three treasures to seek outside ways; not slandering the three treasures and the scriptures of the three vehicles; not doubting places in the very profound scriptures of the great vehicle where you don't understand them; not discouraging anyone determined on enlightenment or causing them to tend to self-enlightenment; not causing uninspired people to go into the lesser vehicles of self-enlightenment; not speaking hastily about the great vehicle in front of those following the lesser vehicles or wrong ideas; not inspiring false ideas; not saying in the presence of outsiders that you have the wonderful precepts of enlightenment; not doing anything harmful or useless to sentient beings. A second set: not abandoning the true teaching; not giving up the spirit of enlightenment; not being stingy with the teachings; not doing anything that is not beneficial to sentient beings; not slandering any of the teachings of the three vehicles; not begrudging teachings; not having false

views, like nihilism; encouraging people not to give up their aspiration for enlightenment; not preaching unsuitable teachings to people without consideration of their faculties; not giving people anything that will harm them.

8. The four holy states are sainthood (arhat), self-enlightenment (pratyeka-buddha), bodhisattva, and buddhahood.
9. The ten realms are born of a single moment of thought.

Sermon of Zen Master Bassui

If you want to avoid the pains of transmigration, you should directly know the way to become enlightened. The way to become enlightened is to realize your own mind. Since your own mind is the fundamental nature of all sentient beings, which has never changed since before your parents were born, before your own body existed, it is called the original face.

This mind is originally pure: when the body is born, it shows no sign of birth; and when the body dies, it has no sign of death. Neither is it marked as male or female, nor has it any form, good or bad. Because no simile can reach it, it is called the enlightened nature, or Buddha nature.

Furthermore, all thoughts arise from this inherent nature like waves on the ocean, like images reflecting in a mirror. For this reason, if you want to realize your inner mind, first you must see the source of thoughts arising. Whether awake or asleep, standing or sitting, deeply questioning what thing is your inner mind with the profound desire for enlightenment, is called practice, meditation, will, and the spirit of the way. Questioning the inner mind like this is also called zazen.

One moment seeing your own mind is better than reading ten thousand volumes of scriptures and incantations a day for ten thousand years; these formal practices form only causal conditions for a day of blessings, but when those blessings are exhausted again, you suffer the pains of miserable forms of existence. A moment of meditational effort, however, because it leads eventually to enlightenment, becomes a cause for the attainment of buddhahood.

Even someone who has committed the worst crimes is a buddha if he instantly transforms and becomes enlightened, but that doesn't mean that you should do wrong on the pretext that you should become enlightened; when you delude yourself and degenerate into evil ways, even the buddhas and patriarchs can't help you. It's like the case of a child sleeping next to its father, having a bad dream about being beaten or falling sick; though he calls to his parents to help him in his distress, since they can't go into his dreams, even his father and mother cannot help him. Even if they are going to give him medicine, they have to wake him up. If a man can awake on his own he can avoid suffering in dreams without the help of others; in the same way, if you realize that your own mind is Buddha, you can suddenly avoid repeated involvement in routines of birth and death. If the buddhas could help us, how could anyone go to hell? You must realize the truth of this yourself.

Now, then, when you look what is the host, the master who is now seeing colors, hearing sounds, raising hands and moving feet, though you realize that all this is the doing of your own mind, actually you don't know what its inner reality is. If you say it is nonexistent, yet it is clear that it is free to act; if you say it exists, yet its form cannot be seen. As it is simply inconceivable, with no way at all to understand, when your ideas are ended and you are helpless, this is good work; at this point, if you don't give up and your will goes deeper and deeper, and your profound doubt penetrates the very depths and breaks through, there is no doubt that mind itself is enlightened. There is no birth and death to detest, no truth to seek; space is only one's mind.

For example, it is like getting lost in a dream, losing the road to return home, asking people or praying to gods and buddhas to find the way back, until you awaken, when you find you've been in your own bedroom all along; then you realize that there was no other way to return from your dream journey except to awaken. This is called "returning to the fundamental," and it is also called "birth in the world of peace and ease."

This is a way of understanding through attainment of power from a little bit of cultivation; everybody who cultivates meditation and works at it, whether householders or homeless, has at least such experience. This already is beyond the ken of people who do no meditation. This is already real enlightenment, but if you think you have no doubts about reality, you're greatly mistaken. This would be like giving up the search for gold when you see copper. When you have such a tendency, you should resolutely deepen your effort by observing your body as an illusion, like a bubble, like a reflection and see your mind as like space, with no form. Here, hearing sound in the ear, what is the host that cognizes the echo? Tenaciously, profoundly, wholly doubting, when no cognizable principle exists anymore and you have forgotten about the existence of your body, when your former views and understanding die out and your doubt has become complete, your enlightenment will be complete, just as no water remains in a bucket when its bottom falls out. It will be like a dead tree bursting suddenly into bloom. If you can be like this, you will realize freedom in the midst of things and become greatly liberated.

But even if you have such an enlightenment, you must give up every enlightenment you realize and time and again return to the awakening host, go back to the fundamental; if you can guard it firmly, as sentimental consciousness dies out, your inherent nature will become clear just as a jewel becomes more lustrous with polishing; eventually it will illumine the worlds in all directions. Don't doubt this; if your determination is not deep, even if you don't awaken in this way in this life, people who face death in the midst of meditation will surely become enlightened easily in the coming life, just as a journey prepared for yesterday is easily traveled today.

When working on sitting meditation, don't suppress the arising of thoughts, but don't enjoy it; just search out the inner mind, source of thought. Realizing that whatever drifts through the mind or appears to the eyes is illusory, not real, you shouldn't fear, esteem, like, or dislike; if your mind is like empty space not affected by things, then when you die also you will not be attacked by the devil of heaven. Also, when doing meditation work, it should only be a question of what your own mind is, without keeping such-and-such a thing or such-and-such a principle on your mind.

Also, when you realize what the host is who hears

all sounds right now, this mind is the fundamental source of all buddhas and sentient beings. Kannon is called Seer of the Sounds of the World because she attained enlightenment by way of sound. Just see what it is that hears this sound, whether standing or sitting, look for this; when you don't know what you're hearing anymore and your direction is ended and you are diffused and far out, even here as long as sound is being heard, when you look deeper and deeper, even the appearance of vague diffusion dies out and it is like a clear cloudless sky. Herein there is nothing that can be called self. The host who hears cannot be seen, either. This mind is the same as universal space, yet there is no place that can be called space. At this time you think this is enlightenment, but you should doubt even more; who hears this sound? If you go on investigating without producing a single thought, the realm where seems like nothing exists, like empty space, also dies out, there is no more taste at all; where it is dark as night, if you exert all your power to fully doubt what it is that hears this sound, then when the doubt shatters and you are like someone who has completely died coming back to life, this then is enlightenment, *satori*.

Sayings of Zen Master Bunan

People see others in terms of themselves. The vision of fools is dreadful. If there is ambition in oneself, one will see others on the basis of that frame of mind. He who lusts looks with lust. Unless one is a sage, seeing is dangerous. Even though there are people on the great way, people who can see and know are rare. What a waste. A wise man discerns the potential of others, though they may not be equal to him, and makes use of their level of understanding.

To acquiesce to the teaching of enlightenment, as it is, directly abandon all things, merge with the body of thusness and experience peerless peace and bliss, is no more than a matter of whether or not you think of the body. Although there are people who think this teaching is true, it's hard to find someone who strives to make it his own.

It is easy to keep things at a distance; it is hard to be naturally beyond them.

There are no mountains to enter outside of mind, making the unknown your hiding place.

While deluded, one is used by this body; when enlightened, one uses this body.

• *Asked of the supreme vehicle, Bunan said,*

To let the body be free and not to cling to anything. For this reason it is a great matter; thus it is a rare thing in this age.

Whether man or woman, you should first make them see reality, and have them sit in meditation for that; when their seeing of reality is complete, then you should teach them to respond to any event.

When virtually enlightened, have them preserve that, so that bad thoughts do not arise; if they nurture this for a long time, they will become people of the way.

When virtually enlightened, if you teach them that all things are it, most people will turn bad. Those who only preserve enlightenment mostly are trapped in sitting meditation and become devotees of discipline. Whether it's good or bad to expound the great way immediately depends on who you're talking to. You must teach with understanding, not misunderstanding.

You should always act with kindness and compassion. People think that kindness and compassion mean doing things, but actually giving people things is the foremost kindness and compassion. Never to do or say what is painful to others is kindness and compassion.

When you do things which are unpleasant and painful to others, even if you have a mountain of treasure it will eventually be ruined. There is no doubt about this. Thus, working diligently, there comes to be no Buddha, no teaching; though living you are not here, neither do you die, you don't remain in this world or go to the next world—having become like empty space, you don't even think of empty space. There is no body, nothing at all—there is no thought of nothingness or of being.

O my body,
Used to being used at will,
Since there is no using body or me.

Fire is something that burns; water is something that wets; a buddha is someone who practices compassion. Teaching people to be kind and compassionate to others means imitating the Buddha. If you just practice compassion, you will certainly become good. The basis of compassion is purity of the mind. Purity of the mind is "not a single thing." "Not a single thing" means nothing at all; it is beyond the reach of speech, beyond affirmation and negation. If there is any affirmation or negation in your heart, it will be obstructed by that affirmation and negation; if there is no affirmation or negation, then heaven and earth are one. If there is something, it separates you from heaven—this you should well understand.

The mind which knows nothing
Is a Buddha
By a different name.

Since you will surely eventually die, you should set your mind diligently on the way of enlightenment.

There is no enlightened Buddha outside your own heart; always keep a pure and clean mind and heart. When thoughts of your own body come up, as long as such bad thoughts are always there, this life is but a little while and you will fall into a hell and suffer forever and ever; but even leaving that aside, in this life you will suffer in many ways.

When the heart is pure and compassionate, there is no Buddha outside of this.

Once you have been greatly enlightened, there is no great enlightenment; when praying, there is no prayer; when rejoicing, there is no one to rejoice. Living, there is nothing living; dying, there is nothing that dies; there is nothing existent or nonexistent. Though you have physical form, you have no form; beyond being and nonbeing, you let existence and nonexistence be, beyond affirmation and negation, you let right and wrong be—

While deluded,
It is things that are things;
When enlightened,
You leave things to their thingness.

Things People Are Always Wrong About:

Hating to be fooled by others while liking to be fooled by oneself.

Knowing others die but not realizing one's own death.

Discriminating others' right and wrong while not acting properly oneself.
Suffering from want and not knowing how to avoid it.
Thinking that original nothingness is nothing.
Setting up something in the way of enlightenment.
Unless you enter the way of enlightenment, you cannot preserve your body.
There are those who perform memorial services without respecting the Buddha in their own bodies.
Considering enlightenment to be the teaching of the Buddha—those who are enlightened are rare.
Not knowing how to overturn bad impulses.

• *Bunan's Regulations for Disciples*

A monk is the greatest evil on earth; he goes through the world without labor—he is a great thief.

When the fruits of discipline and practice are fulfilled and one may be a teacher of others, he is a precious jewel in the world. There are innumerable teachers of the ways of the world, but teachers of the Great Way are rare.

Do not use unwisely even a piece of paper or half a penny.

Be constantly austere with the body, and do not do things for the sake of the body. The enemy of Dharma and Buddha is the body.

Look upon accepting things from others as like poison. When you have completely realized the great way, then you should accept those things which people hold dear; this is because it helps those people.

During the period of practice and effort, should you be beaten and trampled by others, you should rejoice that the effects of the deeds you yourself produced in the past are being exhausted.

When master Joshu was asked if a dog has enlightened nature or not, he said No. If you can really understand this No, you will surely be free from doubts about anything in or out of this world. For example, when you first enter, you shatter being and nothingness. Having shattered being and nothingness, if you nurture it energetically, you break through the body. Having broken through the body, if you work hard, you break through the mind. Having broken through body and mind, the original mind appears. When you reach that, then there is no doubt about what the world-honored Buddha taught: there are hells; there are heavens; there are enlightened ones and devils, hungry ghosts and animals; there is retribution. You will have no doubts at all about the scriptures.

As for fundamental nothingness, when for example they sit and meditate people think that control of body and mind is the basis of "not a single thing," but they are all wrong. "Originally not a single thing exists" refers to the absolute nonexistence of "body" and "mind." When you reach here, paradises and hells spoken of by the Buddha are certain; hungry ghosts and animals certainly exist. Those who don't reach here talk in various ways to become well known, but since it doesn't come from truth, their words and actions are not in accord.

Bunan used to say to his group,

There is no special principle in the study of the way; it's only necessary to see and hear directly. Directly seeing, there is no seeing; directly hearing, there is no hearing. You must fuse inside and outside into one solid thoroughly peaceful state before you can do this.

Although you people are buddhas right now, yet you don't realize it. If you know you go against the buddhas and patriarchs, if you don't know you revolve in the routine of birth and death. At this point, if you don't have the transcendental eye, how can you attain realization?

Knowing the fundamental,
Detached from myriad things;
Who knows that which is outside words,
Which the Buddhas and Patriarchs didn't transmit?

Although our school considers enlightenment [satori] in particular to be fundamental, that doesn't necessarily mean that once you're enlightened you stop there. It is necessary only to practice according to reality and complete the way. According to reality means knowing the fundamental mind as it really is; practice means getting rid of obstructions caused by habitual actions by means of true insight and knowledge. Awakening to the way is comparatively easy; accomplishment of practical application is what is considered most difficult. That is why the great teacher Bodhidharma said that those who know the way are many, whereas those who carry out the way are few. You simply must wield the jewel sword of the adamantine sovereignty of wisdom and kill this self. When this self is destroyed, you cannot fail to reach the realm of great liberation and great freedom naturally.

If you can really get to see your fundamental mind, you must treat it as though you were raising an infant. Walking, standing, sitting, lying down, illuminate everything everywhere with awareness, not letting him be dirtied by the seven consciousnesses. If you can keep him clear and distinct, it is like the baby's gradually growing up until he's equal to his father—calmness and wisdom clear and penetrating, your function will be equal to that of the buddhas and patriarchs. How can such a great matter be considered idle? Now the reason that we consider human life best is for no other reason than being means to realize true liberation in this lifetime. However, if you seek profit and support, considering these the ultimate truth, in every moment of thought used by delusive ideas, vainly ending your life, at the time of death nothing you can do will be any use. The Buddha came into the world to guide those on the paths of illusion, directly pointed to the fundamental mind, letting them leave behind birth, death, and myriad things. While this body clearly exists, clearly realizing this body doesn't exist, while there are clearly seeing, hearing, discernment and knowledge, clearly realizing there are no seeing hearing discernment or knowledge—this is called the effect of true investigation; how could it be easy?

When you go near fire, you are warm; when you go near water, you are cool; and when you go near people imbued with the way, they naturally make your mind die and conceptions dissolve, causing all wrong thoughts to cease. This is called the spiritual effect of complete virtue. You all call yourselves people of the way as soon as you enter the gate. Really, you should be ashamed.

Sayings of National Teacher Bankei

The master said to an assembly,

What I tell people about is nothing special; it's the unborn enlightened mind innate in everyone. What is it about? While you're all here listening to my sermon, when a dog barks outside the temple you know it's a dog, and when a crow caws you know it's a crow. And also you can distinguish the colors black and white, and see the difference between men and women—even though you are not thinking about hearing dogs or crows or seeing black, white, men, or women, during the talk, nonetheless right here you can see and hear them all before conceptually discriminating them. Then even if a thousand or ten thousand people should tell someone that a dog's bark is a crow's caw, that person would hardly be deceived by them. Isn't this enlightened mind, with its inconceivable qualities of clear awareness, something to be grateful for?

Because people don't know that everyone has such wonderful qualities and powers they get confused by one thing and another. That confusion ultimately arises from self-importance. Self-importance means, for example, that you get angry and upset when you hear your neighbor criticize you, and only dislike and maltreat that person; this is because of self-importance. Also when you hear your neighbor praise you, you think well of that person, and act nicely; this, too, is because of self-importance.

Considering the root source of this self-importance, when people are born they have no bad thoughts of hatred or liking for anyone; it's just that as they grow up they learn and cultivate various bad things and bad thoughts by seeing and hearing them, piling them up into mental habits. Always putting these mental habits to use, various kinds of confusion and error begin.

Hating people or being jealous of them is the condition of hell; anger and rage is the condition of demonia; lustful thoughts of greed and stinginess are the condition of hungry ghosts. Regretting afterward and longing for what's ahead is folly, the condition of animals. These are called the four bad dispositions. These bad dispositions are not inborn at all; originally there is only the unborn enlightened mind. But because of the outside dust of mental habits, the most important enlightened mind is turned into the bad conditions of hells and whatnot. Born in the honorable human state, taking the quality of clarity which discerns good and bad, right and wrong, and turning it into something worthless, is a miserable, pitiful thing, is it not?

I set my heart on the way of enlightenment since youth, sought teachers everywhere, sometimes sat all the time without lying down, sometimes lived in the mountains, doing various difficult and painful practices, finally to awaken to the root source of the enlightened mind; but you all are lucky, to have deep affinity with the enlightened ones, that you can sit here without doing any practice and hear how to attain buddhahood easily.

A layman asked,

Though I'm grateful for your teaching of birthlessness, thoughts from constantly applied mental habits readily come up, and I get lost in them and have difficulty remaining continually unborn. How can I apply wholehearted faith?

The master replied,

If you try to stop arising thoughts, the stopping mind and the stopped mind become split in two and you never have any peace of mind. Just trust that thoughts are originally nonexistent but temporarily arise and cease conditioned by what is seen and heard, and have no real substance.

A layman asked,

By ignorance and folly one becomes an animal, going from darkness into darkness, unable to realize buddhahood, so I hear; but when an animal doesn't know in its own heart that it is miserable and doesn't cognize his condition as painful, after all can't he be happy?

The master replied,

To transform the enlightened mind and body innate in everyone into the miseries of hell, yet not to realize how wretched that is, is a sad thing, is it not? For example, when you beat and scold a dog who took a chicken the day before, even though he doesn't realize it is happening because he took the chicken yesterday, he certainly howls and suffers when he gets punished. Because he is an animal, he doesn't know the principle of cause and effect and gets pain from pain without limit. Because knowledge is clear in human beings, when they meet a guide, they can easily realize enlightenment. Are we not grateful to be born in a human body, easy to accomplish buddhahood with? This one great matter is right before your eyes; don't waste time.

A layman asked,

When I wipe out arising thoughts, they keep coming up from the traces, never stopping. How can I control these thoughts?

The master replied,

Wiping out arising thoughts is like washing blood with blood; though the first blood may be removed, the washing blood still stains; no matter how much you wash, the stain is not removed.

This mind is originally unborn and undying and without illusion; not realizing this, thinking that thoughts are existent things, you roam around in the routines of birth and death.

Realizing that thoughts are only temporary appearances, you should let them be as they start and stop, without grasping or rejecting them. It is like images reflected in a mirror; since the mirror is clear and bright, it reflects whatever comes before it but doesn't keep the images. The enlightened mind is infinitely brighter and clearer than a mirror and is also radiantly aware, so all thoughts dissolve in that light without leaving a trace. If you can believe and trust in this truth, no matter how much they come up it won't be a hindrance.

A farmer asked,

I was born with a short temper and am easily stirred to angry thoughts. As a farmer, I get involved in my work and find it hard to become unborn. What should I do to realize the unborn mind?

The master replied,

Because everyone is the innate unborn enlightened mind, there is no way to realize it now for the first time; just doing a farmer's tasks without other thoughts is called the activity of the unborn mind.

When you're hoeing, you can talk to people and still hoe at the same time; getting involved in conversation does not make you unable to hoe. You can even hoe when you're mad, but as anger is a bad condition of hellish existence, the task is difficult and painful. If you hoe without any delusions like anger, it is easy to do, pleasant work; this is the activity of the enlightened mind, unborn undying activity.

A monk asked,

The ancestral teachers since ancient times were greatly enlightened through difficult and painful practices, and I have heard that you, too, accomplished the great teaching through various difficult practices. But people like me, who don't cultivate practice and are not enlightened, just realizing that my very state is the unborn enlightened mind does not really settle anything.

The master replied,

It's like the case of travelers who cross the peaks of high mountains where there is no water and become thirsty. Someone seeks out water in a distant valley, breaking his back searching here and there. Finally he finds water and brings it back to give to the others to drink. Even though they have not struggled so, those who drink are refreshed just the same as the one who went through the trouble before. As for those who are doubtful and will not drink, there is no way for their thirst to be quenched.

Because I didn't meet someone with enlightened eyes, I mistakenly wore myself out, finally discovered the buddha in my own mind, and am telling everyone about the buddha of their own mind without them having to do anything difficult, just like drinking water and having their thirst quenched.

Using the enlightened mind inherent in everyone just as it is, having found peace and bliss without the difficulties of confusion—is this not a sacred true teaching?

A monk asked,

All wild thoughts of mundane passions are hard to subdue; how can they be quieted?

The master replied,

Thinking of trying to annihilate wild thoughts is also wild thought. Although wandering thoughts are originally nonexistent, they are produced by your own conception.

Someone asked,

Though I don't doubt that there are no confused thoughts in reality, thoughts come up all the time and it's hard to become unborn.

The master replied,

That's because although you were only the unborn enlightened mind when you were born, as you grew up you saw, heard, and learned the mentality of ordinary people and over a long period of time became deluded by familiarity to the point where the deluded mind has become independent and self-willed.

Because thoughts are not originally inborn, they die out in the mind which accepts and trusts the unborn buddha of the mind itself. For example, when someone fond of alcohol gets sick and can't drink liquor, even when the opportunity to drink is there and he wants to, as long as he doesn't drink the liquor it won't affect his illness and he won't get drunk; thus by abstaining even in the midst of his desire, he eventually becomes free from sickness. Confused thoughts are also like this—if you let them be as they come and go, and do not act upon them or dislike them, wandering thoughts will in no time disappear in the unborn mind.

Someone asked,

Last year when I asked you how to stop the arising of mixed-up thoughts, you told me to let thoughts be as they arise and cease. Afterward, faithfully trying to put this into practice, it's hard to get to let them be as they arise and cease.

The master replied,

It's hard to attain because you think there is a rule to let thoughts be as they arise and cease.

The Soto Zen master Yuie came to see Bankei and asked,

I was inspired when I was seventeen or eighteen, and for over thirty years have sat long without sitting, becoming single-minded; yet errant thoughts and deceptive consciousness are hard to erase. In recent years, my mind and knowledge have been clear, and I have realized peace. How did you apply your mind in the past?

The master Bankei replied,

When I was young, I, too, had a lot of trouble with thoughts, but I suddenly realized that the source of our school is the enlightened eye; and even among the ancients there was none who helped people as long as his own eyes were not clear. From the beginning, transcending all considerations of self, I worked only on attainment of the enlightened eye. For this reason, I can freely discern whether people have the eye or not.

Someone asked about zazen (sitting meditation); the master replied,

Zazen means merging with the inconceivable wisdom innate in everyone, before getting involved in considerations and discriminations—this is called zen, "meditation"; outward detachment from all things is called "sitting." Just sitting with your eyes closed is not sitting meditation; only sitting in communion with inconceivable knowledge is worthwhile meditation.

All delusion is routine misunderstanding because of relying on thoughts. When angry thoughts appear, you become demons; lust makes animals; greed makes hungry ghosts. If you die without giving these up, you'll wander around forever, taking on all sorts of forms, revolving in birth and death. But when you are detached from thought, because there is no confusion there is no cause and effect; and because there is no cause and effect, there is no transmigration.

While you have thoughts, if you practice virtue there will be good causes and effects; and if you do evil, there will be bad causes and effects. If you detach from thought and harmonize with inconceivable knowledge, there are no causes or effects of birth and death. Now, when I speak this way, it may seem like a view of nothingness, nothing at all, but it is not so; the reason is that when I speak this way, you all hear—even though you have no particular thought of hearing this, because the original knowledge inherent in everyone is aware and clear, you can hear distinctly. When you touch fire or water, everybody knows without learning that fire is hot and water cool because this is activity apart from thought, even though without thought it cannot be said to be nothing. This fundamental inconceivable knowledge is beyond the dual idea of existence and nonexistence and freely communes with all things, like a clear mirror distinctly reflecting the images of things.

Thus, what conceptualization do you need? Conceptualization is discrimination because of confusion; if you reach nonconceptual knowledge, you illumine and distinguish things before conception and never get confused. Therefore we esteem nonconceptual knowledge. Therefore the sitting meditation of unborn inconceivable knowledge is considered the highest practice. Zen folk don't set up expressions and analyze principles, talking about secondary things; for this reason, Buddhism is sometimes criticized for being a far-out teaching, beyond the conventions of human society and lacking social consciousness. But this criticism is because of failure to realize the basis of the path. The reason that social virtues exist in name is that there are antisocial thoughts and teaching is established to encourage virtue. If you reach the state of no delusion, what lack of social virtue is there? Antisocial behaviour is because of confusion, and confusion is judgment and discrimination. In a person without discriminatory thoughts, what antisocial feeling can there be?

Once the master said,

When I first set out to realize enlightenment, I did a lot of painful austerities because I didn't meet a good teacher and friend, wasting away; sometimes I cut off all contacts with humanity and lived in seclusion, sometimes I sat inside paper enclosures or in dark rooms behind screens—never lying down, sitting cross-legged, my thighs festered, leaving scars which still remain. Also, when I heard there was a man of knowledge someplace in some province, I would go there directly to meet him. I did this for several years, walking through most of Japan; all this was because I didn't meet an enlightened teacher. After my mind opened one day, I realized for the first time that my years of effort and pain were useless, and I found peace.

Now I tell you about how you can attain realization without breaking your backs, but you don't really believe completely; this is because you are not really earnest for truth.

Also once he said,

The inner truth which I discovered when I was living in a hermitage when I was twenty-six did not differ in the slightest from the truth when I met the Chinese Zen master Daoje and got his testimony of enlightenment, or right now, today. However, as far as complete illumination of the eye of objective reality and mastery of the supreme teaching and realization of great freedom is concerned, I am as different now from when I met Daoje as sky is from earth. Believing in and acting on this, you should seek the day of fulfillment of the eye of reality.

Someone asked,

Is the complete illumination of the eye of reality accomplished with time and season, or is it realized even in one day?

The master replied,

It is not a matter of time and season; it is accomplished only when the eye of the way is clear, without any gap. It is accomplished by the practice of single-minded devotion to nurturing it.

Issan, one of Bankei's senior disciples, once asked,

Is reading the Buddha's scriptures and patriarchs' records of use in studying the way?

The master replied,

There is a time for reading the records of the patriarchs. When you read seeking the truth of the scriptures and records, you blind your own eyes; when you read with insight into the truth, they provide proof.

In 1684, during a retreat at Korinji in Tokyo, one day in the meditation hall Issan had an overwhelming transformation of state and went to see Bankei alone. He said,

Up till now I have believed your teaching and been fooled by your words. Today I don't depend on the teacher's words; I have come to know my own business directly. Even so, all this is just what you have always been saying. It's hard to express in words.

The master replied,

Even though you don't say it, I know it.

Issan said,

You always say there is no such thing as great enlightenment, but today as I see by myself, if people don't have their own knowledge they cannot apprehend the truth. Already Rinzai was in Obaku's community, where he asked three times about the essential meaning of the teaching of the enlightened ones and was beaten each time, but still didn't discover anything. However, at one word from Daigu he was transformed and said that really there is not much to Obaku's Buddhism—this was Rinzai's own knowledge.

The master said,

The change that took place at Daigu's was Rinzai's point of entry. Those who study and investigate Zen, past and present, all have entry sometime; however, if you stop there, you have gotten a little and consider it enough. After this, if you are not most earnest it will be hard to accomplish the complete illumination of the eye of reality.

Issan said,

I do not presume to doubt your statement, but I now have no doubts about the truth; there is no way to apply effort beyond this.

The master said,

It is easy to get to the state where there is no doubt and no questioning, but the truth is exceedingly profound, knowledge and wisdom extremely deep; the farther you go, the deeper they are. For this reason it is my custom not to give a lifetime's approval at one word. Most important, if you watch an enlightened guide, your realization will grow deeper and deeper.

Issan said,

I humbly hear your command. In the past when I read the Altar Scripture of the Sixth Patriarch, in the paragraph on Nangaku, the Sixth Patriarch says, "What thing thus comes?"

Nangaku said, "To liken it to something would miss it."

The patriarch said, "Then can it be cultivated and realized or not?"

Nangaku said, "It's not that there are no practice and realization, but if defiled, you won't attain."

The patriarch said, "Just this nondefilement is what all the buddhas safeguard; you are thus and I am thus."

The Sixth Patriarch's witness of Nangaku was in the realm which only a buddha can share with a buddha. However, Nangaku attended the Sixth Patriarch for fifteen years, daily going further into the mysterious profundity; since it is the sphere communicated by a buddha only to a buddha, I wondered what reaching of mysterious depths there could be, but now by the master's knowing words my former doubts have stopped.

Issan once asked Bankei,

I have always had many mental habits; should I stop them by always keeping my mind concentrated?

Bankei answered,

If you just realize that mental habits are originally nonexistent, what will you stop?

Issan said,

I certainly agree without doubt that mental habits are originally nonexistent; but even so, in my present daily experience, should I concentrate my mind on this?

Bankei answered,

That is not really agreeing.

Issan said that after faithfully applying the master's kind words, he verified this in experience.

Jakua was the abbot of Bukkoin temple in Ikaruga; a tiger of the doctrines of the Tendai school, he was quite famous. At the urging of the local people, he went to Ryomon Temple to see Bankei; after repeated questions and answers he eventually submitted to Bankei. One time when he went to Ryomon, as he was about to return, Bankei said to Jakua, "Do you hear the sound of the bell of the neighboring temple?"

Jakua, not understanding, went back to his own temple; for ten days he was fused into one solid whole during all his activities, when suddenly he heard the bell of the neighboring temple. He went that very day to Ryomon hoping to be approved by master Bankei.

Bankei came out and said, "You have heard the sound of the temple bell."

Jakua agreed and then spoke to Bankei of it. Also, when he wanted to lecture on the interpretation of the four teachings in Osaka at the request of the Tendai groups there, he went to Bankei and told him of his intent. Bankei raised one finger and said, "How would you explain this scripture?" Jakua had no reply.

Afterward, Jakua changed his vestments and entered Ryomon Temple as one of Bankei's disciples. Eventually he became recognized as the first of Bankei's enlightened disciples.

Zeshin dwelt in a hermitage on Mt. Yoshino for a long time, just sitting. One morning his mind opened and he forgot all knowledge. In a nearby temple there was an elder of the Soto school, to whom he went to present his understanding. The elder told him that master Bankei was the enlightened guide of the present generation and told him to go see him.

Zeshin went right to Jizo temple east of Kyoto, but Bankei was in seclusion and not seeing anyone. Zeshin came every day and sat outside the gate till evening, when he would return to the capital; he did this for thirteen days, when the proprietor of the inn where he stayed directed him to another master, Dokusho. Zeshin went and presented his understanding to Dokusho, who just told him to protect it well. Zeshin then went back to Yoshino, where he stayed for several months.

Zeshin set out again for Kyoto to see Bankei, when he heard that Bankei was staying in Tokyo. Zeshin went to Korin Temple in Tokyo, where Bankei saw him right way and Zeshin offered his understanding. Bankei said, "And ultimately?"

Zeshin hesitated and hung his head. This happened three times, when Zeshin said, "Is there an ultimate?"

Bankei said, "You don't know how to use it."

Zeshin again hesitated and lowered his head. After three times like this, Zeshin finally said, "How to use it?"

At that moment, an oriole cried in the garden; Bankei said, "When the oriole cries, you hear it." Zeshin leaped for joy and bowed three times.

Bankei said, "After this, don't open your mouth in vain."

At the end of the summer, Bankei returned to Ryomon Temple, and Zeshin also went there. For several days, as Bankei interviewed new arrivals, Zeshin also came and sat before the master, but Bankei didn't deal with him at all. For three days he appeared and so did Zeshin, but Bankei said nothing. Finally, after the crowd had gone, Bankei said to Zeshin, "You're lucky—if you hadn't met me, you would have become a braggart."

Explication of the Four Knowledges of Buddhahood by Hakuin

Some ask, "Are the three bodies and four knowledges inherent, or are they in the sphere of knowledge attained after awakening? Are they realized all at once or are they cultivated gradually?"

The answer is that although these are fundamentally complete in everyone, unless brought to light, they cannot be realized. When the student has accumulated effort in study and investigation and the enlightened nature suddenly appears, all at once he realizes the essence of inner reality; when one is actualized, all are actualized. But though one reaches the stage of buddhahood without passing through steps and stages, if one doesn't cultivate practice gradually, it is impossible to fulfill omniscience, independent knowledge and ultimate great enlightenment.

What does realization at once mean? When the discriminating mind is suddenly shattered and the enlightened essence suddenly appears, the filling of the universe with its boundless light is called "the great perfect mirror knowledge, the pure body of reality." This is the transmuted eighth [storehouse] consciousness.

That all things in the six fields of sense—seeing, hearing, discernment, and knowledge—are your own enlightened nature, is called "the knowledge of equality, the fulfilled body of reward."

Discerning the principles of things by the light of true knowledge is called "the subtle analytic knowledge"; this is the body of reward and also includes the transformation body.

Coughing, spitting, moving the arms, activity, stillness, all doings in harmony with the nature of reality is called "knowledge of accomplishing tasks." This is called "the sphere of freedom of the transformation body."

However, even so, still your seeing the way is not yet perfectly clear and your power of shining insight is not yet fully mature. Therefore, if you don't cultivate practice, you will be like a merchant who keeps his capital and doesn't engage in trade; so he not only never gets rich, but eventually goes broke spending to keep up the pretense of wealth. What do I call gradual practice? It is like a merchant devoting himself to trade, spending a hundred gold pieces to make a thousand in profit, until he accumulates boundless wealth and treasure and becomes free to do what he wants with his blessings. Though there is no difference in the nature of gold, without this business it's impossible to get rich; even if your perception of reality is genuine, when your power of shining insight is weak, you cannot overthrow the barriers of habitual actions. Unless your knowledge of differentiation is clear, you cannot benefit sentient beings in accord with their potentials. Therefore you must know the essential road of gradual practical cultivation.

What is the great perfect mirror knowledge? It means when the beginning student wants to comprehend this great matter, first he must conceive a great will, great faith, and, with the determination to see through the originally inherent enlightened nature, should always question who is the host of seeing and hearing. Walking, standing, sitting, reclining, active or silent, whether in favorable or adverse situations, plunge your spirit into the question of what it is that sees everything here and now? What is it that hears? Questioning like this, pondering like this—ultimately what thing is it? When you keep on doubting continuously, with a bold spirit and a sense of shame surging on, your effort will naturally become unified and solid, turning into a single mass of doubt throughout heaven and earth; the spirit is suffocated, the mind distressed, like a bird in a cage, like a rat that's gone into a bamboo tube and can't escape—at that time, if you keep on going without retreating, it will be like entering a crystal world; the whole mass, inside and outside, mats and ceilings, houses and pillars, fields and mountains, grasses and trees, people and animals, utensils and goods, all are as they are like illusions, like dreams, like shadows, like smoke. When you open your eyes clearly with presence of mind and see with certainty, an inconceivable realm appears which seems to exist yet also seems not to exist in a way. This is called the time when the conscious essence becomes manifest. If you think this is wonderful and extraordinary and joyfully become infatuated and attached to this, after all you will fall into the nests of the two vehicles, outsiders, or troublesome devils, and can never see the real enlightened nature.

At this point, if you do not fondly cling to your state but arouse your spirit to wholehearted effort, from time to time you will experience such things as forgetting you're sitting when you're sitting, forgetting about standing when you're standing, forgetting your own body, forgetting the world around you. Then if you keep going without retreating, the conscious spirit will suddenly shatter and the enlightened nature will appear all at once—this is called "the great perfect mirror knowledge." This is the meaning of complete perfect enlightenment at the first stage of inspiration; you can discern the source of eighty thousand doctrines and their infinite subtle meanings all at once. As one becomes, all become; as one decays, all decay—nothing is lacking, no principle is not complete.

Even so, as a newborn child of Buddha, the initiate bodhisattva reveals the sun of wisdom of the enlightened nature; but the clouds of his doings have not yet been cleared away. Because his power in the way is slight and his perception of reality is not perfectly clear, the great perfect mirror knowledge is associated with the eastern direction and called "the gate of inspiration." It is like the sun appearing in the east; although the mountains, rivers, and land get some rays, they still are not yet warmed by the sunlight. Though one day you see the way clearly, when your power of shining insight is not great and strong, you are prone to hindrance by instinctual and habitual afflictions and are still not free and independent in both favorable and adverse circumstances. This is like someone looking for an ox who may one day see through to the real ox, but if he doesn't hold the halter firmly to keep it in check, sooner or later it will run away.

Therefore, once you see the ox, you make oxherding

methods your main concern; without this cultivation and practice after enlightenment, many people who have seen reality miss the boat. Therefore the knowledge of equality of reality does not linger in the great perfect mirror knowledge; going on and on, you concentrate on practice after enlightenment. First, use the intimate experience of the very essence you have seen to illumine all worlds with radiant insight. When you see something, shine through it; when you hear, shine through what you hear; shine through the five clusters of your own body, shine through the six fields of sense experience—in front and behind, left and right, through seven upsets and eight downfalls, entering absorption in radiant vision of the whole body, seeing through all things internal and external, shining through them, when this work becomes solid perception of reality is perfectly distinctly clear, like looking at the palm of your hand. At this point, using this clear knowledge and insight more and more, entering afflictions you shine through afflictions, entering enlightenment you shine through enlightenment, entering favorable circumstances you shine through favorable circumstances, entering adverse situations you shine through adverse situations; when greed or desire arises, you shine through greed and desire, when anger and hatred arise you shine through anger and hatred, when folly arises you shine through folly. When the three poisons of greed, hatred, and folly cease to exist and the mind is pure, then you shine through that pure mind. At all times, in all places, be it desires, senses, gain, loss, right, wrong, views of Buddha or of Dharma, in all things, shine through with your whole body; if your mind doesn't regress from this, the nature created by your actions naturally dissolves, inconceivable liberation is realized, your actions and understanding correspond, principle and fact merge completely, body and mind are not two, essence and appearance do not obstruct each other—attaining this, managing to attain the realm of true equanimity, is called "the knowledge of the equality of the nature of reality."

This does not mean the nondual merging into one view of equality of signlessness; what is called knowledge of equality of reality refers to the point of true equanimous liberation, realized by constant refinement of one's state. Though the range of the views are equal in principle, in actual fact they are not yet equal; if you get involved in objects of old habitual afflictions, your insight and power in the way will naturally get stuck and you won't be completely free. Therefore this refined practice after enlightenment is called "knowledge of equality of real nature" and is associated with the southern direction and called "the gate of practice." It is like when the sun is over the southern direction, its light full, illumining all hidden places in the deep valleys, drying up even hard ice and wet ground. Though a bodhisattva has the eye to see reality, unless one enters this gate of practice it is impossible to clear away obstructions caused by actions and afflictions, and therefore impossible to attain to the state of liberation and freedom—what a pity that would be, what a loss.

Next, the subtle observing analytic knowledge; having reached the nondual sphere of equality of true reality, the essential point is to clearly understand the profound principles of differentiation of the enlightened ones and master techniques for helping sentient beings. Otherwise, even if you have cultivated and attained unhindered knowledge, you will remain after all in the nest of the lesser vehicle and be unable to realize omniscience, unhindered knowledge, freedom to change in any way necessary to help sentient beings, enlighten youself and enlighten others, and reach the ultimate great enlightenment where awareness and action are completely perfect.

For this reason, it is essential to conceive an attitude of great compassion and commitment, to help all sentient beings everywhere; in order to penetrate the principles of things in their infinite variety, first you should study them day and night through the verbal teachings of the buddhas and patriarchs. One by one ascertaining and analyzing the profundities of the five houses and seven schools of Zen and the wondrous doctrines of the eight teachings given in the five periods of Buddha's teaching career, if you have any energy left over, you should clarify the deep principles of the various different philosophies. However, if this and that get to be a lot of trouble, it will just waste your faculties to no advantage; if you thoroughly investigate the sayings of the buddhas and patriarchs which are difficult to pass through, and clearly arrive at their essential import, perfect understanding will shine forth and the principles of all things should naturally be completely clear. This is called "the eye to read the scriptures."

Now, the verbal teachings of the buddhas and patriarchs are extremely profound and should not be considered exhausted after one has gone through them once or twice. When you climb in the mountains, the higher you climb they higher they are; when you go into the ocean, the farther you go the deeper it is—it's the same in this case. It's also like forging iron to make a sword; it is considered best to put it into the forge over and over, refining it again and again. Though it is always the same one forge, unless you put the sword in over and over and refine it a hundred times, it can hardly turn out to be a fine sword. Penetrating study is also like this; unless you enter the great forge of the buddhas and patriarchs, difficult to pass through, and make repeated efforts at refinement, through suffering and pain, omniscience and independent knowledge cannot come forth. Just penetrating through the barrier locks of the buddhas and patriarchs over and over again, responding to beings' potentials everywhere with mastery and freedom of technique, is called subtle observing analytic knowledge.

This is not investigation by means of intellectual considerations; knowledge to save oneself and knowledge to liberate others, when completely fulfilled and mastered, is called subtle observing analytic knowledge. This is the state of the perfectly fulfilled body of reward; it is associated with the western direction and called the gate of enlightenment. It is like the sun having passed high noon, gradually sinking toward the west. While the great wisdom of equanimity is right in the middle, the faculties of sentient beings cannot be seen and the teachings of differentiations among things cannot be made clear. If you do not stop in the realm of self-enlightenment as inner realization and cultivate this subtle observing analytic knowledge, you have done what you can do; having done your task, you reach the land of rest. This is not the meaning of the sun setting; it has the meaning of accomplishment of all the knowledges, the fulfillment of enlightenment, because enlightening self and others, fulfillment of awareness and action, is considered real ultimate enlightenment.

Next, the knowledge of accomplishment of works; this is the secret gateway of mental command, in the realm of ultimate liberation. This is called "undefiled knowledge" and also "uncreated virtue." If you don't realize this knowledge, you won't be capable of great freedom in doing what is to be done to benefit yourself and others. So what is called effortless? Because the preceding subtle observing analytic knowledge is accomplished by successful practice and is in the realm of cultivation, realization, attainment by study, it is call called knowledge with effort. This knowledge [of active accomplishment] transcends the bounds of practice, realization, attainment through study, and is beyond the reach of indication or explanation. For example, the subtle observing knowledge is like the flower of complete enlightenment and practice blooming; while this knowledge of doing what is to be done is like the flower of complete enlightenment and practice dropping away and the real fruit forming. This you cannot see even in a dream unless you have passed through the final pass of transcendence of our school. That is why it is said that at the final word you come at last to the unbreakable barrier.

The way to point out the direction is not in verbal explanations; if you want to reach this realm, just refine your subtle observing analytic knowledge in the differentiating and difficult to pass through stories, smelting and forging hundreds and thousand of times over and over. Even if you have passed through some, repeat over and over, examining meticulously—what is this little truth beyond all convention in the great matter of transcendence? If you don't regress in your examination of the sayings of the ancients, someday you may come to know this bit of wonder.

Even so, if you don't seek an enlightened teacher and personally enter his forge, you cannot plumb the profound subtleties. The only worry is that real teachers of Zen are extremely few here and hard to find. But if someone exerts his energy to the utmost in this and penetrates through clearly, he attains freedom in all ways, transcends the realms of buddhas and devils, yet roams freely in the realms of buddhas and devils, solving sticking points, removing bonds, pulling out nails and pegs, leading people to the realm of purity and ease. This is called "the knowledge to accomplish works"; it is associated with the northern direction and called "the gate of nirvana." It is like when the sun reaches the northern quarter, when it is midnight and the whole world is dark; reaching the sphere of this knowledge, it is not within understanding or comprehension—even buddhas can't see you, much less outsiders and devils.

This is the thoroughly peaceful state of pure reality of the buddhas and patriarchs, the forest of thorns which patch-robed monks sit, lie, and walk in twenty-four hours a day. This is called "great nirvana" replete with four attributes (self, purity, bliss, eternity), and also called "the knowledge of the essential nature of the cosmos," in which the four knowledges are fully complete. The center has the meaning of totalizing the four knowledges, and the essential nature of the cosmos represents the sense of the king of enlightenment, master of the teachings, being king of the Dharma, free in all ways.

I hope that Buddhists with great faith will conceive great trust and commitment and cultivate the great practice for the fulfillment of these four knowledges and true enlightenment. Don't lose out on the great matter of myriad eons because of pride in your view of the moment.

The Essential Secrets for Entering the Way— Words of Master Torei

In what the Zen school calls ascending directly from the state of ordinary man to buddha, there are five discriminations: one is the meaning of same nature, second the meaning of different paths, third the meaning of urgency, fourth the meaning of progressive practice, and fifth the meaning of returning to the basis. This is the essential road.

First, same nature: the fundamental nature inherent in sentient beings is not other than the fundamental nature of all the buddhas of the past, present, and future. Their range of powers and qualities are also equal, their lights are radiant; their knowledge, wisdom and miraculous powers are all the same. This may be likened to the light rays of the great solar disc shining everywhere on the mountains, rivers, and plains, so nothing is not illumined. Gold and jewels are bright in themselves even when they are in mud. However, blind people do not see, are not aware of this light, even though they are in its very midst; they are to be pitied.

Second, different paths: although in their fundamental nature buddhas and sentient beings are the same substance, no different, the directions of their minds are different. Buddhas shine inward to illumine the basic mind, whereas sentient beings turn outward and get involved with myriad things. That is why sentient beings create greed and lust for things they desire, anger and rage towards people they dislike, and become fools by becoming congealed in their thoughts; confused and stupefied by these three poisons, they have lost their very fundamental mind.

Those in whom greed and lust run deep turn into

hungry ghosts, those in whom anger and rage run deep become antigods, and those deep in folly and delusion become animals; those in whom the three poisons are equal fall into hell and suffer various miseries. These are called the four bad dispositions; they are most dreadful.

Even though they have greed, anger, and folly, those who restrain themselves and are not self-indulgent are human, and in this way will not lose this bodily form life after life. Those in whom greed, anger, and folly gradually quiet down, and who are not self-indulgent even though they don't restrain themselves are born in heaven, known as gods of the six heavens of desire. Those in whom the nature of the three poisons has died out, but though they have qualities of calmness and wisdom, they have views attached to calmness and have residual habits of aversion and ignorance, are born among the eighteen kinds of heaven of pure form. When the love for calmness is done with but one has not yet opened up the knowledge and insight of the enlightened ones, this is called the four formless heavens; those who practice discipleship and self-enlightenment are in these latter heavens. If you are wondering how this all comes about, you create these worlds with your minds deeply afflicted by greed, anger, and folly, producing such bodily forms as a result. Therefore, unless you extinguish these afflictions and their active expressions, you cannot be liberated; unless you are liberated from the world of suffering of these six dispositions, there is no real peace.

If you want to be free from this world of suffering,

first you must contemplate impermanence. Those who are born must inevitably die. Even the young are not exempt; even the strong are in danger. Even the rich and prosperous decline, even the noble and exalted cannot remain that way. Even a long life does not last more than eighty years or so. Thus, this world being impermanent, there is nothing enjoyable. The poor suffer from lack, the rich suffer from possessions, the high suffer from their high status, the low suffer from their low status; they suffer over food and clothing, suffer over wives and children, suffer over wealth, suffer over official rank. Anyway, if you don't annihilate the nature of afflictions somehow and arrive on the path of liberation, even if you ascend to the rank of sovereign of a nation, great minister, deity, spirit, or wizard, it is still evanescent as lightning and morning dew, lasting only for a while.

When conditions meet, everything sure seems to exist; but when the conditions disintegrate, emptiness. This body is gotten through the relationship of father and mother, comes from their conditions—solidity becomes skin, flesh, ligament, and bone; fluidity becomes spittle, tears, pus, and blood; heat becomes warmth and flexibility; air becomes breath and movement. When these four conditions suddenly are exhausted, the body gets cold and the breath stops—there is nothing called "me." At that time this body is really not our own; it is only a temporary inn. How can we be so greedily attached to this temporary inn that we ignore eternity?

Contemplating these four transcendences—impermanence, suffering, emptiness, selflessness—seeking the way of enlightenment, is called "the teaching of four realities, for disciples." This is the essential gateway to beginning entry into the way for all enlightened ones.

Also the twelve causal conditions, for those who can become enlightened by understanding conditionality, are as follows. When the original mind is in the dark, it produces various activities; these are the two [conditions]: ignorance and action. As actions accumulate, they become instinctive; the parents copulate and the embryo dwells within; these are consciousness and name and form. When the body is complete and its six faculties finally developed, this is called "the six media [of sense]." Being born, yet not yet distinguishing good and bad, is called "contact." After the age of two or three, people already enjoy good tastes and beautiful colors; this is called "sensation." After the age of ten, there is longing for goods and sex; this is called "craving." Past fifteen or sixteen, people greedily cling to one thing after another; this is called "grasping." From the age of twenty, when you do your adult work without fear of wrongdoing, is called "becoming." When you are doing what you do and piling up faults, the condition of your future life, for good or bad, is decided therein; this is called "birth." Doing such things all your life, you get old and feeble and die. These are called the twelve causal conditions of human life. Those who are enlightened by understanding these conditions examine them, put an end to passion and affliction, and enter enlightenment. These are all techniques of the enlightened ones for entering the way. When you understand the mind darkened by ignorance and see its real nature, then ignorance becomes identical to the enlightened nature, action is the way, consciousness becomes the power of knowledge. Then the twelve causal conditions all accord with the right way and eventually arrive at the great realization of liberation.

Also the six transcendences of bodhisattvas are generosity, morality, tolerance, effort, meditation, and wisdom. The preceding two gateways of practice, of disciples and those enlightened by understanding conditions, benefit oneself only individually and do not have the principle of helping others. Bodhisattvas include the teaching of others in practicing the way for their own benefit as well. They do not spare their wealth when it is for the true way; they make offerings to teachers and give donations to the poor. This is called "material generosity." According to their own depth of knowledge and virtue, they teach and influence others; this is called "generosity with the teaching." Practicing these two kinds of giving to all sentient beings is called "the transcendance of generosity."

Inwardly guarding your spirit of the way, observing fundamental ethics and their ramifications, is called "the transcendence of morality."

Accepting the truth you see, not affected by circumstances of blame or praise, not giving birth to a single thought of anger or resentment, is called "the transcendence of tolerance."

Growing day by day in the great work of helping yourself and helping others, warding off laziness and diligently progressing, is called "the transcendence of effort."

Concentrating wholeheartedly on directed effort in sitting meditation and becoming free from all illusions is called "the transcendence of meditation."

Exhaustively studying the principles of the teachings and examining the intent of the Buddha, consciously breaking up all delusive feelings, is called "the transcendence of wisdom." These are called "the six transcendences of bodhisattvas."

These practices of disciples, those enlightened through disruption of the causal chain, and bodhisattvas—those who struggle for everyone's enlightenment—are called "the three treasuries"; they are also called "the three vehicles." They are techniques of the buddhas for realizing the path, principles that do not change for a thousand ages. When students of the one vehicle of buddhahood say these are teachings of the three treasuries of the lesser vehicle and reject them, it is to break up the biased view of the lesser vehicle and awaken them to the wonderful truth of the great vehicle. If you believe in the wonderful truth of the great vehicle, then the gateways of practice of the three vehicles are all helpful wings of the great vehicle. It is like the case of the people and slaves, who are of lower class than the lords and rulers; when the people and slaves are rejected, the lords and rulers lose their authority. Because the people are many, the ruler is noble. Because of the fulfillment of the lesser vehicles, the great vehicle is broad and far reaching. Even the buddhas of the past, present, and the successive generations of enlightened ancestors reached actualization of truth by way of the practical entrances of the three vehicles.

Now people with minds should think clearly; among the pains and troubles of the four bad dispositions, which would you not fear? The blessings and powers of humanity and godhood cannot be relied on either. Anyway, the four realities of disciples are good practice for each of them; everything in this world is misery. Impermanent, it is a desolate house. Whatever may be eventually returns to emptiness. Even one's body is not one's own possession—how much less wives, children, valuables, or kingship, followers, oxen, horses, and so forth! When you die, you go alone; who goes with you? What can you take along with you?

Strangers in the present were parents and children, husbands and wives in former lives; parents and children and husbands and wives of the present are strangers of the future. Oxen, horses, fish, and birds of the present are relatives of former lives; relatives now are oxen, horses, fish, and birds of the future. Drawn by force of actions, following circumstances, it's hard to judge what form of life, what kind of body one may have to experience. Therefore, once you are separated from your parents and children, husbands or wives, those closest to you in the present, you don't know where they are or what they turned out to be. The closeness of bone and flesh even is only for fifty years. It is like deeply loving an overnight guest, disliking other people. When the night is over and the friend leaves, that friend goes east or west, wandering on alone. The people you didn't like before become friends for a night.

The only thing worthy of prayer and trust is enlightenment; the only thing to be sought is the actualization of buddhahood. This body is a skin bag of habitual obstructions produced by the twelvefold routine of conditioning. First you must break up the root of ignorance; once the root is broken, the branches and leaves cannot remain. Practice generosity with goods and teaching, according to your means. Keep the Buddha's precepts without violating them. Tolerate people and don't become angry. Pray and pledge to the buddhas and spirits morning and night; progress diligently without forgetting thought after thought. If you have free time, sit in meditation. When you hear the true teaching, consciously break through illusion. These are the practices of the six transcendences of bodhisattvas.

Although their fundamental natures are the same, buddhas turn inward while sentient beings run outward—from this moment of error, they have divided into sentient beings of nine realms; hell beings, hungry ghosts, antigods, humans, and deities, the six dispositions, and disciples, those enlightened by conditions, and bodhisattvas, the three vehicles. This is the meaning of different paths. If you return to the source, these are of the same substance as the buddhas; is this not to be hoped for?

Third, the sense of urgency means that if you want to realize the same nature of all buddhas, first you must clearly understand the root of ignorance. This is done by questioning your own fundamental nature. How to do this? Seeing colors with the eyes, hearing sounds with the ears, feeling cool and hot with the body, discerning pleasant and unpleasant in the mind. This is called seeing, hearing, awareness, knowing; these are the seeds of practice. Ordinary people get confused by form when they see it, get confused by sound when they hear, get confused by cold and hot when they feel, get confused by pleasant and unpleasant when they cognize; this is what I call "sentient beings turning outward."

As for the practice of bodhisattvas, when they see forms, they question what it is that sees; when they hear, they question what hears; when they feel, they question what feels; when they cognize, they question what cognizes. This is what I call the "buddhas turning inward." When you practice like this, your orientation is different from that of ordinary people, as mentioned before—it is the same as the orientation of the buddhas, and even if you don't fully realize their wisdom and powers, you should realize that a fledgling bodhisattva has entered the intermediate state.

Always make great vows to the buddhas, pray to the spirit luminaries and make pledges to the ancestral teachers; in this way fulfill the great matter once and sport in the ocean of vows to help self and others. When you get up in the morning, no matter how hurried you are, first arouse this one thought; try this meditation work in seeing and hearing, and after that go about your business. When you eat, make this thought first and try this meditation. When you go to the toilet, make this thought first and try this meditation. When the day is over and you are going to bed, first sit awhile in bed with this thought foremost; try this meditation before lying down to sleep. This is the practice of the true and straight road of the buddhas and bodhisattvas. Disturbed by the fact that you have lost the original nature which is of the same substance as all the buddhas and come to wander through the six dispositions and four kinds of birth, turn to your fundamental nature and urge on your meditational efforts. This is called "the sense of urgency.

Fourth, the meaning of progressive practice means that as you urge on your meditation on the fundamental as just described, you should progress moment after moment, practicing in everything. Summoning forth the state of correct mindfulness in meditation, when you walk you practice while walking, when you rest you practice while resting; when speaking with people you practice while speaking, and when silent and quiet urge on your correct mindfulness all the more. When seeing things, doubt the seer; when hearing things doubt the hearer; when things are busy and it's easy to get distracted, doubt that which is distracted; when you question what it is that gets distracted, then even when distracted you do not lose the right mindfulness of your meditation effort. When sick, you should use your misery as a seed of meditation effort. Anyway, even when things are busy, this, too, should be a way of progressing in meditation; if things are quiet all the time, there won't be energy in your meditation. Without energy in meditation, there is no empowerment.

When quelling disturbance in the country, when everything is at stake and in the midst of the danger of battle you fight back and forth without fear, that is when you win victory. The Dharma battle of meditation work is also like this; when distracted by various things and disturbed by various thoughts, that is a good time to decide victory or defeat. In this frame of mind, without laziness, you should progress. When things are quiet, this is really a matter of practicing military arts inside the castle; so understanding, you should cultivate practice with utmost sincerity. When things are busy, this is the time to decide victory or defeat on the field of battle; so understanding, you should concentrate your effort on directing meditation. Even if you don't attain power, in doing this, in both cases you will be people prepared for the straight and true road of the buddhas and bodhisattvas.

For example, someone in the prime of life is able to walk miles a day, whereas someone who is weak can walk only a short way. In going to a distant country, the strong one may easily get there in a few days, while the weak one may take a few weeks; nevertheless, once they are arrived they are in the same country, among the same people. Whether one has sharp or dull faculties or disposition is like this, too; it is the same as being sickly and having a hard time getting there or being strong and going with ease—depending on whether people are sharp or dull, whether their faculties are strong or weak, there will be differences in how quickly or slowly they become enlightened and find the way. [But] when it comes to the attaining of the way through practice, there is no difference. Should we not take this opportunity? I hope that whether you are smart or stupid, noble or mean, you will make preparations for journey on the way by this direct practice.

There is another meaning within this progressive practice; when effort is pure and ripe, without thinking of it or considering it, you will find empowerment. Even though you get power, you shouldn't be lazy about cultivating practice. If you concentrate energy, empowerment comes of itself, so there are great and small empowerments; lesser enlightenment, after all, turns out to be a hindrance to great enlightenment. If you give up lesser enlightenments and don't cling to them, great enlightenment will surely be realized. If you grasp little enlightenment and don't relinquish it, great enlightenment will surely be ignored. This is like someone so greedy for a little profit that he doesn't get a big profit; if he doesn't cling greedily to a little profit, great profit will eventually be realized; if he accumulates small profits, eventually it will amount to great profit.

If you cling to a lesser benefit and do not progress, spending your whole life within the limits of only a small realization, you can't reach the realm of great freedom and great liberation. Unless you arrive at great enlightenment and find the path of great freedom, fact and principle do not harmonize, so you enter into outside paths with false views. This is dreadful. Once you have some small enlightenment, if you use this as a seed to progress further and further, the great reward of all the buddhas will be revealed. You pass naturally through the barrier locks of the ancestral teachers, fact and principle truly accord, with action and understanding not different, you reach the sphere of great liberation and great independence. This is called "the essential secret of progressive practice."

Exhausting the inner principles of all things, perfecting all virtues of the way as a benefactor of all sentient beings everywhere, explaining the truth, teaching and influencing according to potential and situation yet without anything lacking, one arrives together with others at the shore of four qualities (self, purity, bliss, eternity) of great nirvana. With this great practice and great vow, make self-help and helping others your task in every life in every world, never turning back for all time.

In the meantime, though you may make mistakes

and regress, if your legs are weak and the road slippery, you fall and you'll die there if you don't get up; yet if you keep getting up when you fall and keep going on, eventually you'll get there. When it says in the scriptures that when we commit a fault we should repent right away before the buddhas, and again proceed on the path, this is what it means.

Fifth, the meaning of returning to the basis; as the work previously described progresses and your practice becomes wholly mature, eventually you return to the nature of the same one substance of all the buddhas. This is called fulfilling buddhahood. This is what is referred to in the Zen schools as seeing real nature and fulfilling buddhahood. When the first thought goes wrong and instead of turning inward to the basic mind it ranges outward to myriad objects, floating and sinking in the six paths of hells, hungry ghosts, animals, antigods, humans, and gods, lives apart, generation after generation, revolving in these routines for a thousand lives over myriad eons, like the wheel of a cart. We have experienced the same pains and troubles countless times; if the bones of every life were piled up, they would be higher than a mountain, and if their pus and blood were stored, they would be more than the waters of the ocean; so the realized one has explained.

Now, having a human body, so difficult to get, and having encountered the teaching of enlightenment, which is especially hard to encounter, and therein to have heard the inconceivable true teaching of the great vehicle, is the greatest fortune anyone can have. If you mistakenly ignore this, it would be the greatest wrong you can do. It is said that once you lose the human form, it is as hard to get it again as to drop a thread from the highest heaven to thread a needle at the bottom of the ocean with it.

Also, the routines of transmigrations in the six ways of life are not only a matter of other lives; even in one day there is floating and sinking. Those whose minds are upright and actions not evil are humans; when they get angry at opposition, they are antigods. If they cling to things they like, they are hungry ghosts. When their minds are stifled by worry and longing, they are animals. When their longings are deep and their greedy attachments are strong and the flames of their rage never die down as they pain people and harm beings, they are hell fiends. This is called losing the human form and creating the seeds of the three mires.

Then, again, sometimes the mind is still. There is no anxiety, and the heart is clear throughout. Then it is said that even though the body is in the human realm, the mind roams in heaven. Thus in one day an ordinary person transmigrates countless times, during which he rarely keeps the human mind, much less roams in heaven. To begin with, they wander mostly in the three mires of animal anxiety, ghostly greed, and ungodly wrath; often they enter hellish ways, causing suffering to people and injuring beings. Truly we should see how much we wander in what paths in the course of a day.

First of all, the mentalities of the evil ways are two parts of three; humans keep one part, and hell is also mixed in there. So even in the ordinary state of mind, these bad ways are hard to avoid. In this one day, arouse the determination to cultivate practice of the four realities of disciples, of the method of contemplation of the twelve causal conditions as the self-enlightened ones do, and of the great way of the six transcendances of the bodhisattvas; with this mind, you should cut off the seeds of the three mires. Those who work to progress in the effort of the great vehicle, even if they don't yet attain enlightenment, eliminate the mentality of the three mires, transcend the sport of humans and gods, and climb into the ranks of the bodhisattvas.

Even disciples and self-enlightened ones should be honored; how much more the way of bodhisattvas. Even the way of bodhisattvas is a rare fortune; how much more so the teaching of the one vehicle of buddhahood. Seeing reality and realizing the path is the crowning meditation of the buddhas; those who set their minds on this are direct children of Buddha. In every moment of consciousness they carry out unexcelled practice of virtue; with every step they reach the ineffable action of transcendent wisdom. As far as wisdom is concerned, even the merit of reading or reciting words of wisdom is great; how much the more so to carry them out!

Even having others read and recite prevents danger of disasters; how much the more for those who actually practice themselves! The buddhas will rejoice; the bodhisattvas will take their hands; the spirits of sky and earth will protect these people; malicious ghosts and spirits will be frightened just seeing their shadows. Psychic energies and unseen spirits, when coming in contact with such people, will conceive the thought of obtaining the seed of liberation. This is called "the most worthy and most eminent, the foremost teaching"; it should be practiced to the best of one's ability.